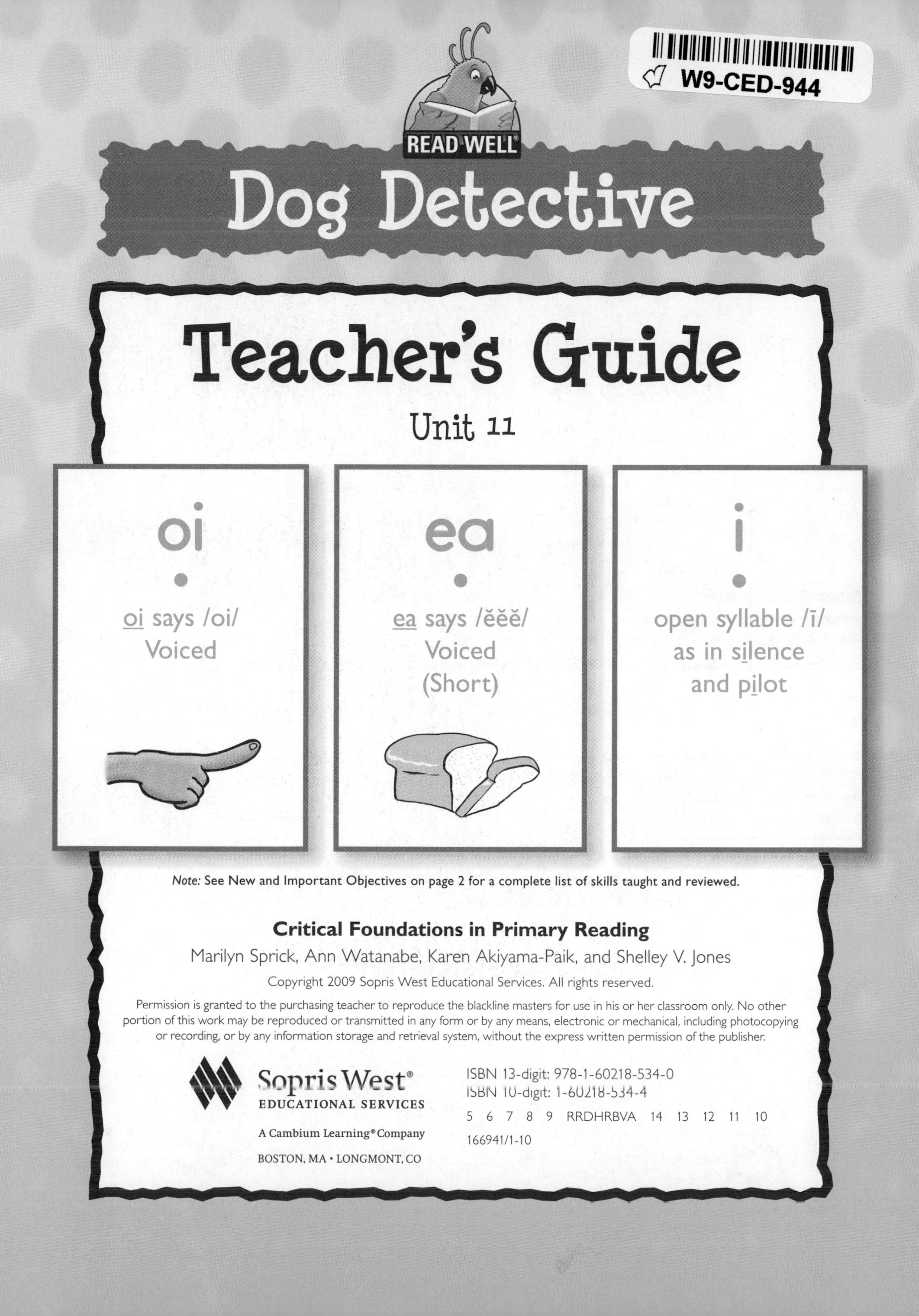

Note: See New and Important Objectives on page 2 for a complete list of skills taught and reviewed.

Critical Foundations in Primary Reading

Marilyn Sprick, Ann Watanabe, Karen Akiyama-Paik, and Shelley V. Jones

Sopris West® EDUCATIONAL SERVICES

A Cambium Learning® Company

BOSTON, MA • LONGMONT, CO

ISBN 13-digit: 978-1-60218-534-0
ISBN 10-digit: 1-60218-534-4

5 6 7 8 9 RRDHRBVA 14 13 12 11 10

166941/1-10

Table of Contents

Unit 11

Dog Detective

How to Teach the Lessons

End of the Unit

Letter Sounds and Combinations

Cumulative Review of *Read Well 1* Sounds and Combinations (Ss, Ee, ee, Mm, Aa, Dd, th, Nn, Tt, Ww, Ii, Th, Hh, Cc, Rr, ea, sh, Sh, Kk, -ck, oo, ar, wh, Wh, ĕ, -y as in fly, Ll, Oo, Bb, all, Gg, Ff, Uu, er, oo as in book, Yy, a schwa, Pp, ay, Vv, Qq, Jj, Xx, or, Zz, a_e, -y as in baby, i_e, ou, ow as in cow, ch, Ch, ai, igh, o_e, ir) and:

Unit	Sound	Pronunciation	Key Word	Type
Unit 2	aw	/aw/	Paw	Voiced
Unit 3	ew	/o͞o/	Crew	Voiced
Unit 3	ue	/o͞o/	Blue	Voiced
Unit 3	u_e	/o͞o/	Flute	Bossy E Voiced
Unit 5	ow	/ōōō/	Snow	Voiced (Long)
Unit 6	ge	/j/	Page	Voiced
Unit 6	-dge	/j/	Badge	Voiced
Unit 7	ci	/sss/	Circle	Unvoiced
Unit 7	ce	/sss/	Center	Unvoiced
Unit 8	kn	/nnn/	Knee	Voiced
Unit 8	ph	/fff/	Phone	Unvoiced
Unit 10	oa	/ōōō/	Boat	Voiced (Long)
Unit 11	oi	/oi/	Point	Voiced
Unit 11	ea	/ĕĕĕ/	Bread	Voiced (Short)
Unit 12	gi	/j/	Giraffe	Voiced
Unit 12	au	/au/	Astronaut	Voiced
Unit 13	oy	/oy/	Boy	Voiced

Affixes (including morphographs—affixes taught with meaning) and Open Syllables

Cumulative Review of *Read Well 1* Affixes (-ed, -en, -es, -ing, -ly, -s, -y, -tion) and:

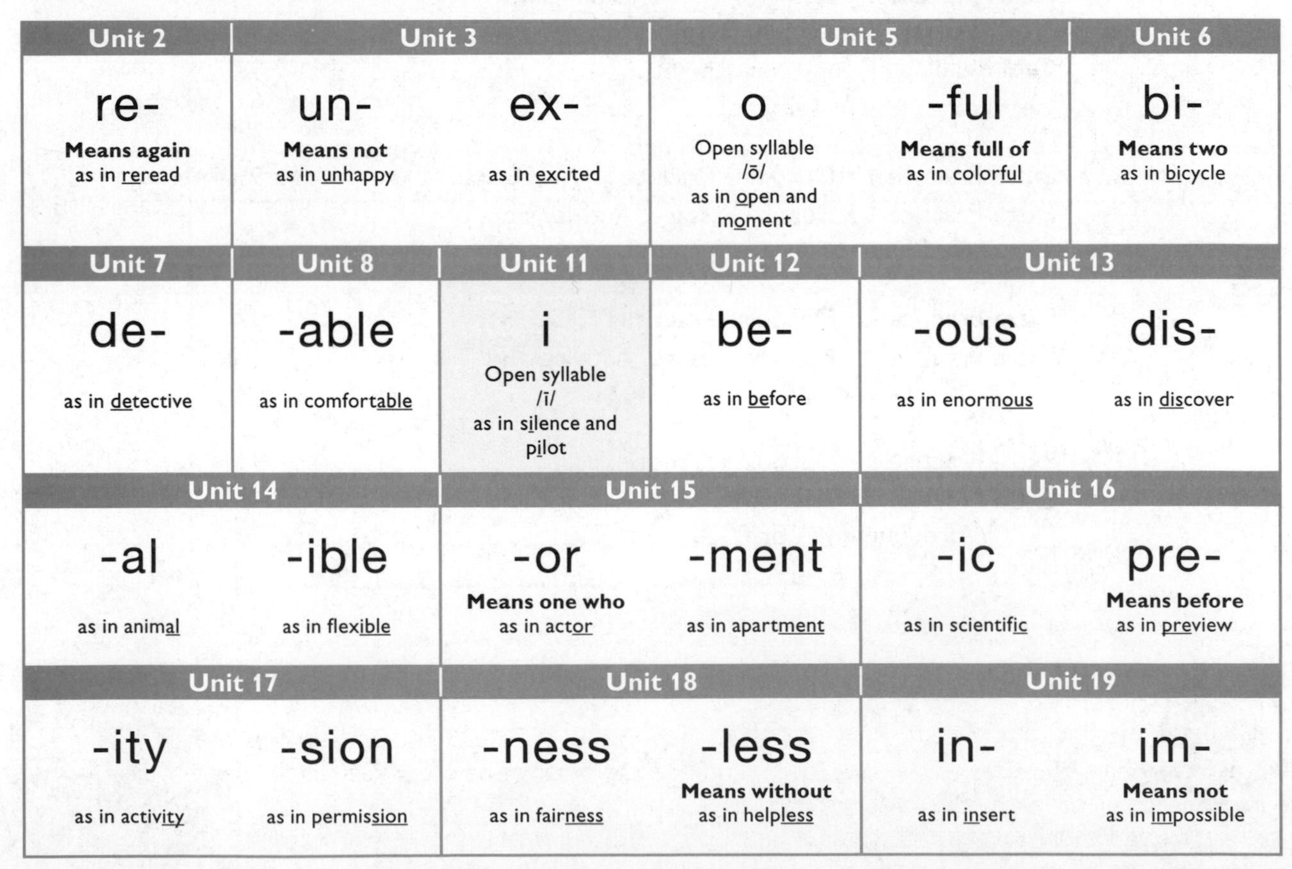

Unit	Affix	Meaning	Example
Unit 2	re-	Means again	as in reread
Unit 3	un-	Means not	as in unhappy
Unit 3	ex-		as in excited
Unit 5	o	Open syllable /ō/	as in open and moment
Unit 5	-ful	Means full of	as in colorful
Unit 6	bi-	Means two	as in bicycle
Unit 7	de-		as in detective
Unit 8	-able		as in comfortable
Unit 11	i	Open syllable /ī/	as in silence and pilot
Unit 12	be-		as in before
Unit 13	-ous		as in enormous
Unit 13	dis-		as in discover
Unit 14	-al		as in animal
Unit 14	-ible		as in flexible
Unit 15	-or	Means one who	as in actor
Unit 15	-ment		as in apartment
Unit 16	-ic		as in scientific
Unit 16	pre-	Means before	as in preview
Unit 17	-ity		as in activity
Unit 17	-sion		as in permission
Unit 18	-ness		as in fairness
Unit 18	-less	Means without	as in helpless
Unit 19	in-		as in insert
Unit 19	im-	Means not	as in impossible

Introduction
Dog Detective

Story Notes

Unit 11 continues the theme of dinosaurs, moving from nonfiction to fiction with a classic mystery.

Sue Goes Missing: A frantic museum director, a disgruntled T. rex, and a dog detective are all the ingredients needed for a big case. When his prize T. rex disappears, museum director Ross calls in Sir Winston to solve the case.

Dog Detective Succeeds: Read all about it! When something big happens, it hits the newspapers. The Case of the Missing Dino is a big deal indeed.

Sue, the Real Story: This series of fictional stories about Sue was first inspired by the real discovery of a T. rex in South Dakota—the largest, most complete T. rex ever discovered.

Recommended Read Alouds

The *Read Well 2* suggested Read Alouds enhance small group instruction—providing opportunities to further build background knowledge and vocabulary.

CAUTION
(Reminder)
Do not read the Read Aloud recommendations during small group instruction. Reserve this time for students to read.

Detective LaRue: Letters from the Investigation
by Mark Teague

Fiction • Mystery

This is a charming mystery about a dog falsely accused and thrown in jail, two missing cats, and a wave of canary burglaries! The tale is told through a series of letters from Ike to his owner.

***Read Well* Connections**

Students will enjoy the contrast between the styles of two very different dog detectives.

NOTE FROM THE AUTHORS

JELL-WELL REVIEWS

Truly low-performing students may periodically need a systematic review—what *Read Well* teachers have come to call a Jell-Well Review. If students begin to hit a plateau in their fluency scores, it will be worth taking the time to go back to do a quick and firming review. See *Getting Started: A Guide to Implementation* to learn how to shore up skills.

New and Important Objectives

A Research-Based Reading Program

Phonemic Awareness
Phonics
Fluency
Vocabulary
Comprehension

Phonological and Phonemic Awareness

Segmenting; Blending; Rhyming; Onset and Rime;
Counting Syllables

Phonics

Cumulative Letter Sounds and Combinations

Review • Ss, Ee, ee, Mm, Aa, Dd, th, Nn, Tt, Ww, Ii, Th, Hh, Cc, Rr, ea, sh, Sh, Kk, -ck, oo, ar, wh, Wh, ĕ, -y (as in fly), Ll, Oo, Bb, all, Gg, Ff, Uu, er, oo (as in book), Yy, a (schwa), Pp, ay, Vv, Qq, Jj, Xx, or, Zz, a_e, -y (as in baby), i_e, ou, ow (as in cow), ch, Ch, ai, igh, o_e, ir, aw, ew, ue, u_e, ow (as in snow), ge, -dge, ci, ce, kn, ph, oa

Cumulative Affixes, Morphographs, and Open Syllables

Review • -ed, -en, -er, -es, -est, -ing, -ly, -s, -y, -tion, re-, un-, ex-, o, -ful, bi-, de-, -able

★New Letter Sounds, Combinations, Affixes, and Morphographs

oi (as in point) • boil, coil, coin, join, noise, oil, point, pointed, soil, spoil, toilet, voice

ea (as in bread) • heavy, instead, measure, measured, sweat, thread, spreads

i (as in silence and pilot) • bimonthly, item, microphone, pilot, scientific, silent

★New Proper Nouns

August, Chicago Times, December, Director Ross, Director Ross's, Pam, Sir Winston's, South Dakota, Tish

★New Contractions

she'll

* **Known Pattern Words With Affixes**, **Known Tricky Words With Affixes**, and **Known Multisyllabic Words With Affixes** have base words students have previously read. The words are new in this unit because they have not been previously read with the affix.

★ = New in this unit

Phonics *(continued)*

★New Pattern Words

age, bald, brow, burst, calm, calmed, calmly, camped, cliff, cliffs, crisp, day, flash, flashed, flashes, flown, hurt, length, lifted, male, milk, paced, per, perk, perking, phrase, quart, rise, roared, rub, rubbed, scent, skull, skulls, sore, spice, spot, storm, stormed, tail, throat, tick, wiped

*__Known Pattern Words With Affixes__ • barked, begging, bored, camped, charged, cleared, clearly, crossed, drinks, eater, eats, faces, gems, lifted, lights, loaded, loads, neatly, pounds, scars, stated, sticking, tracking, unglued, unharmed, usable

★New Compound and Hyphenated Words

afterword, birthmarks, nickname, notepad, truckloads

★Other New Multisyllabic Words

awhile, description, details, difference, difficult, director's, distance, estimated, exhibit, exhibits, fellow, flattered, frantic, kidnapped, kidnappers, lazy, master, mummies, mummy, mystery, paragraph, photographers, replied, reply, responded, simply, specific, succeed, succeeds, tattoos, undisturbed, wacko

*__Known Multisyllabic Words With Affixes__ • appears, cameras, celebrations, finished, following, glistened, located, reporters, stations, supporting, surprisingly

★New Tricky Words

figured, guy, height, serious, shoved, straight, tons, worth

*__Known Tricky Words With Affixes__ • listening, lovable, other's, removed, reviewed, searched, solves, sons, specialty, swarmed, unsolved, woman's

Fluency

Accuracy, Expression, Phrasing, Rate

Vocabulary

New • frantic, specialty, undisturbed

Review • ancient, boast, commotion, contented, crouch, curious, determined, disappointed, distressed, embarrassed, extinct, fossil, hesitate, imagination, imagine, insist, ordinary, weary

Reviewed in Context • adventure, ancient, boast, colony, commotion, determined, dinosaur, distressed, expedition, extinct, fossil, glisten, habit, herbivore, imagination, imagine, locate, ordinary, perfect, plead, realize, remains, roam, senses, splendid, weary, wonderful

Idioms and Expressions

New • come unglued

Review • save the day

Reviewed in Context • leave no stone unturned

Comprehension

Unit Genres

Fiction • Imaginative

Nonfiction • Expository

Comprehension Processes

Build Knowledge: Factual, Procedural, Conceptual

Day	1	2	3	4	5	6
Remember						
Defining			C			
Identifying (recalling)	S,C	E,S,C	E,S,C	S,C	S	S,C
Using	S		C			S
Understand						
Defining (in your own words)	S,C					
Describing	S	S,C	S,C	C	C	C
Explaining (rephrasing)	S	S	S	S,C	S,C	S
Illustrating	C	C			C	
Sequencing				C	C	
Summarizing				C	C	S
Using	S,C	S	S			C
Visualizing	S,C	C			C	
Apply						
Demonstrating						
Explaining (unstated)	S	S	S	S		
Illustrating		C				
Inferring	S,C	S,C	S	S		C
Making Connections (relating)	S					
Predicting	S		S	S		
Using	S,C		C	S		
Analyze						
Classifying	S	E				
Comparing/Contrasting						
Distinguishing Cause/Effect		S				
Drawing Conclusions			S		S	
Inferring						
Evaluate						
Making Judgments						
Responding (personal)		S		S	C	
Create						
Generating Ideas			E,S,C			

E = Exercise, S = Storybook, C = Comprehension & Skill

Comprehension *(continued)*

Skills and Strategies

Day	1	2	3	4	5	6
Priming Background Knowledge						
Setting a Purpose for Reading	S	S	S			
Answering Questions	S	S,C	S	S	S	S
Asking Questions						
Visualizing	S,C	C			C	
Comprehension Monitoring/Fix Ups						
Does it Make Sense?	C	C	C			
Looking Back						
Restating						
Summarizing						
Main Idea						
Retelling					C	
Supporting Details						
Understanding Text Structure						
Title, Author, Illustrator	S,C	S		S		
Fact or Fiction						
Genre (Classifying)	S			S		
Narrative						
Setting	C			C	C	
Main Character/Traits (Characterization)*	S,C	S		C	C	C
Goal				C		
Problem/Solution	S	S		S,C	C	C
Action/Events/Sequence	S		S,C	C	C	C
Outcome/Conclusion				S,C	C	
Lesson/Author's Message						
Expository						
Subject/Topic	E	C	E			
Heading						
Supporting Details (Facts/Information)	E	C				
Main Idea	E	C				
Using Graphic Organizers						
Chart						
Diagram (labeling)						
Hierarchy (topic/detail)		C				
K-W-L						
Map (locating, labeling)						
Matrix (compare/contrast)						
Sequence (linear, cycle, cause and effect)			C			
Story Map				C		
Web				C		

E = Exercise, S = Storybook, C = Comprehension & Skill

* Narrator

Comprehension *(continued)*

Study Skills

Day	1	2	3	4	5	6
Alphabetical Order	C					
Following Directions						
Locating Information	C	C	S			
Note Taking		C				
Previewing						
Reviewing		S	S	S		
Test Taking						C
Using Glossary						
Using Table of Contents	S					
Viewing	S,C					
Verifying						

Writing in Response to Reading

Day	1	2	3	4	5	6
Sentence Completion		C			C	C
Making Lists						
Sentence Writing		C		C	C	C
Story Retell/Summary					C	
Fact Summary						
Paragraph Writing			C		C	
Report Writing						
Open-Ended Response						
Creative Writing						

Writing Traits

(Addressed within the context of Writing in Response to Reading)

Day	1	2	3	4	5	6
Ideas and Content						
Elaborating/Generating					C	
Organization						
Introduction						
Topic Sentence			C			
Supporting Details			C			
Sequencing					C	
Word Choice						
Sophisticated Words (Tier 2 and 3)			C		C	C
Conventions						
Capital	C	C		C	C	C
Ending Punctuation	C	C	C	C	C	C
Other (commas, quotation marks)	C					
Presentation						
Handwriting	C				C	C
Neatness	C				C	C

E = Exercise, S = Storybook, C = Comprehension & Skill

Daily Lesson Planning

LESSON PLAN FORMAT

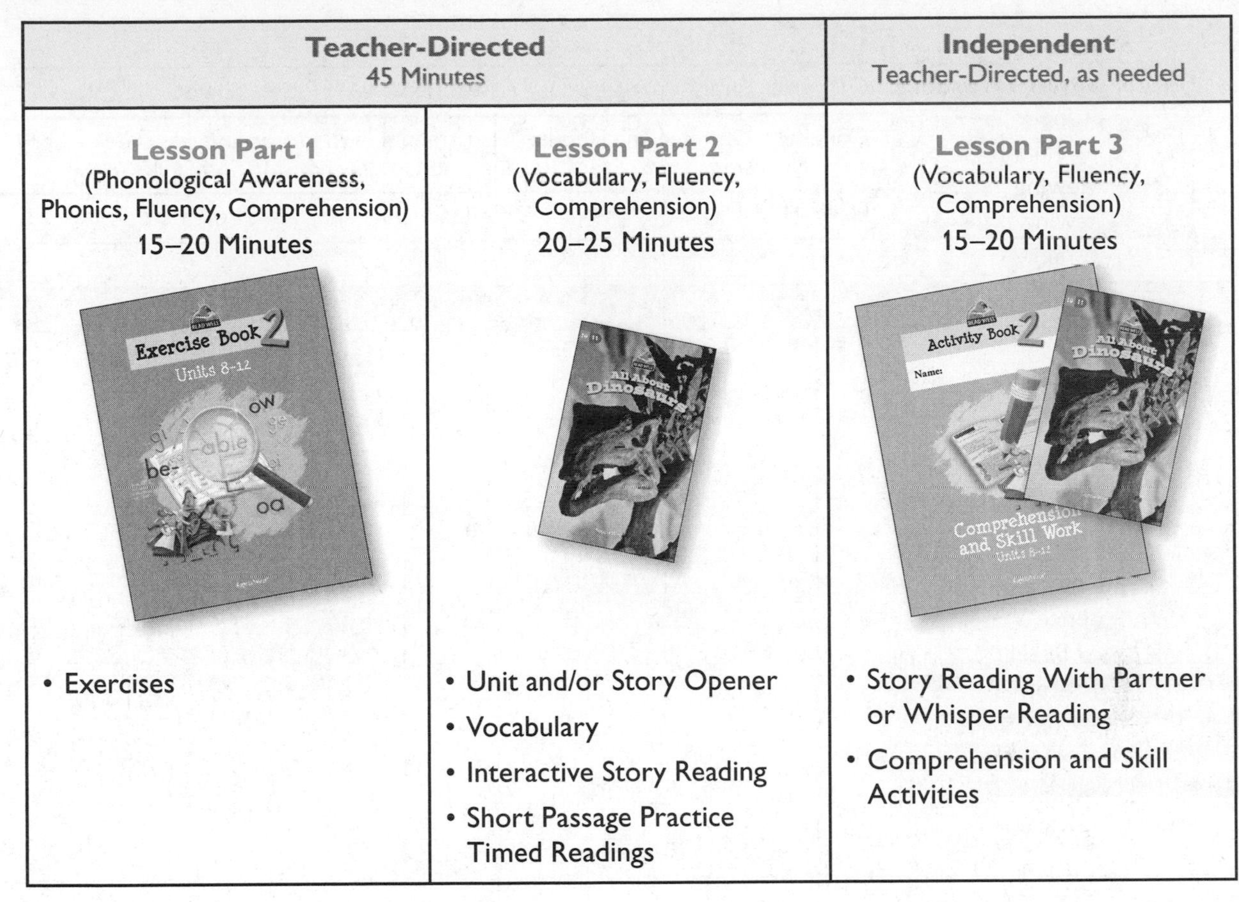

Teacher-Directed 45 Minutes		Independent Teacher-Directed, as needed
Lesson Part 1 (Phonological Awareness, Phonics, Fluency, Comprehension) 15–20 Minutes	**Lesson Part 2** (Vocabulary, Fluency, Comprehension) 20–25 Minutes	**Lesson Part 3** (Vocabulary, Fluency, Comprehension) 15–20 Minutes
• Exercises	• Unit and/or Story Opener • Vocabulary • Interactive Story Reading • Short Passage Practice Timed Readings	• Story Reading With Partner or Whisper Reading • Comprehension and Skill Activities

HOMEWORK

Read Well Homework (blackline masters of new *Read Well 2* passages) provides an opportunity for children to celebrate accomplishments with parents. Homework should be sent home on routine days.

ORAL READING FLUENCY ASSESSMENT

Upon completion of this unit, assess each student and proceed to Unit 12, as appropriate.

WRITTEN ASSESSMENT

During the time students would normally complete Comprehension and Skill Activities, students will be administered a Written Assessment that can be found on page 71 in the students' *Activity Book 2.*

Note: See Making Decisions for additional assessment information.

DIFFERENTIATED LESSON PLANS

The differentiated lesson plans illustrate how to use materials for students with various learning needs. As you set up your unit plan, always include *Read Well 2* Exercises and Story Reading on a daily basis. Unit 11 includes 6-, 8-, 9-, 10-, and 11-Day Plans.

Plans	For groups that:
6-DAY	Complete Oral Reading Fluency Assessments with Passes and Strong Passes
8-DAY	Complete Oral Reading Fluency Assessments with Passes and require teacher-guided assistance with Story Reading and Comprehension and Skill Work
9-, 10-, or 11-DAY	Have difficulty passing the unit Oral Reading Fluency Assessments

6-DAY PLAN

Day 1	Day 2	Day 3
Teacher-Directed • Exercise 1 • Unit and Story Opener: Dog Detective, Sue Goes Missing • Vocabulary, Ch. 1, 2 • Sue Goes Missing, Ch. 1 • Guide practice, as needed, on Comp & Skill 1, 2 **Independent Work** • On Your Own: Partner or Whisper Read, Sue Goes Missing, Ch. 2 • Comp & Skill 1, 2 **Homework** • Homework Passage 1	**Teacher-Directed** • Exercise 2a • Exercise 2b: Focus Lesson • Sue Goes Missing, Ch. 3 • Guide practice, as needed, on Comp & Skill 3, 4 **Independent Work** • On Your Own: Partner or Whisper Read, Sue Goes Missing, Ch. 4 • Comp & Skill 3, 4 **Homework** • Homework Passage 2	**Teacher-Directed** • Exercise 3a • Exercise 3b: Focus Lesson • Sue Goes Missing, Ch. 5 • Guide practice, as needed, on Comp & Skill 5, 6 **Independent Work** • On Your Own: Partner or Whisper Read, Sue Goes Missing, Ch. 6 • Comp & Skill 5, 6 **Homework** • Homework Passage 3
Day 4	**Day 5**	**Day 6**
Teacher-Directed • Exercise 4 • Sue Goes Missing, Ch. 7 • Guide practice, as needed, on Comp & Skill 7, 8 **Independent Work** • Repeated Reading: Partner or Whisper Read, Sue Goes Missing, Ch. 7 • Comp & Skill 7, 8 **Homework** • Homework Passage 4	**Teacher-Directed** • Exercise 5 • Fluency, Dog Detective Succeeds • Guide practice, as needed, on Comp & Skill 9a, 9b **Independent Work** • Repeated Reading: Partner or Whisper Read, Dog Detective Succeeds • Comp & Skill 9a, 9b **Homework** • Homework Passage 5	**Teacher-Directed** • Exercise 6 • Fluency, Sue: The Real Story **Independent Work** • Repeated Reading: Partner or Whisper Read, Sue: The Real Story • Written Assessment • Oral Reading Fluency Assessment* **Homework** • Homework Passage 6

* The Oral Reading Fluency Assessments are individually administered by the teacher while students are working on their Written Assessments.

8-DAY PLAN • *Pre-Intervention*

Day 1

Teacher-Directed
- Exercise 1
- Unit and Story Opener: Dog Detective, Sue Goes Missing
- Vocabulary, Ch. 1, 2
- Sue Goes Missing, Ch. 1
- Guide practice, as needed, on Comp & Skill 1

Independent Work
- Repeated Reading: Partner or Whisper Read, Sue Goes Missing, Ch. 1
- Comp & Skill 1

Homework
- Homework Passage 1

Day 2

Teacher-Directed
- Review Exercise 1
- Review Vocabulary, Ch. 1, 2
- Sue Goes Missing, Ch. 2
- Guide practice, as needed, on Comp & Skill 2

Independent Work
- Repeated Reading: Partner or Whisper Read, Sue Goes Missing, Ch. 2
- Comp & Skill 2

Homework
- Homework Passage 2

Day 3

Teacher-Directed
- Exercise 2a
- Sue Goes Missing, Ch. 3
- Guide practice, as needed, on Comp & Skill 3

Independent Work
- Repeated Reading: Partner or Whisper Read, Sue Goes Missing, Ch. 3
- Comp & Skill 3

Homework
- Homework Passage 3

Day 4

Teacher-Directed
- Exercise 2b
- Sue Goes Missing, Ch. 4
- Guide practice, as needed, on Comp & Skill 4

Independent Work
- Repeated Reading: Partner or Whisper Read, Sue Goes Missing, Ch. 4
- Comp & Skill 4

Homework
- Homework Passage 4

Day 5

Teacher-Directed
- Exercise 3a
- Exercise 3b: Focus Lesson
- Sue Goes Missing, Ch. 5
- Guide practice, as needed, on Comp & Skill 5, 6

Independent Work
- On Your Own: Partner or Whisper Read, Sue Goes Missing, Ch. 6
- Comp & Skill 5, 6

Homework
- Homework Passage 5

Day 6

Teacher-Directed
- Exercise 4
- Sue Goes Missing, Ch. 7
- Guide practice, as needed, on Comp & Skill 7, 8

Independent Work
- Repeated Reading: Partner or Whisper Read, Sue Goes Missing, Ch. 7
- Comp & Skill 7, 8

Homework
- Homework Passage 6

Day 7

Teacher-Directed
- Exercise 5
- Fluency, Dog Detective Succeeds
- Guide practice, as needed, on Comp & Skill 9a, 9b

Independent Work
- Repeated Reading: Partner or Whisper Read, Dog Detective Succeeds
- Comp & Skill 9a, 9b

Homework
- Comp & Skill Activity 7 (Fluency Passage)

Day 8

Teacher-Directed
- Exercise 6
- Fluency, Sue: The Real Story

Independent Work
- Repeated Reading: Partner or Whisper Read, Sue: The Real Story
- Oral Reading Fluency Assessment*
- Written Assessment

Homework
- Teacher's Choice

9-, 10-, or 11-DAY PLAN • *Intervention*

For Days 1–8, follow 8-Day plan. Add Days 9, 10, 11 as follows:

Day 9 Extra Practice 1

Teacher-Directed
- Decoding Practice
- Fluency Passage

Independent Work
- Activity and Word Fluency A

Homework
- Fluency Passage

Day 10 Extra Practice 2

Teacher-Directed
- Decoding Practice
- Fluency Passage

Independent Work
- Activity and Word Fluency B

Homework
- Fluency Passage

Day 11 Extra Practice 3

Teacher-Directed
- Decoding Practice
- Fluency Passage

Independent Work
- Activity and Word Fluency A or B
- Oral Reading Fluency Assessment*

Homework
- Fluency Passage

Materials and Materials Preparation

Core Lessons

Teacher Materials

READ WELL 2 **MATERIALS**

- Unit 11 Teacher's Guide
- Sound Cards
- Unit 11 Oral Reading Fluency Assessment found on page 93
- Group Assessment Record found in the *Assessment Manual*

SCHOOL SUPPLIES

Stopwatch or watch with a second hand

Student Materials

READ WELL 2 **MATERIALS (for each student)**

- *All About Dinosaurs* storybook
- *Exercise Book 2*
- *Activity Book 2* or copies of Unit 11 Comprehension and Skill Work
- Unit 11 Written Assessment found in *Activity Book 2*, page 71, and on the blackline master CD
- Unit 11 Certificate of Achievement (blackline master, page 94)
- Unit 11 Homework (blackline masters)
  See *Getting Started* for suggested homework routines.

SCHOOL SUPPLIES

Pencils, colors (optional—markers, crayons, or colored pencils)

Make one copy per student of each blackline master, as appropriate for the group.

Note: For new or difficult Comprehension and Skill Activities, make overhead transparencies from the blackline masters. Use the transparencies to demonstrate and guide practice.

FOCUS LESSONS

For Exercises 2b and 3b (Focus Lessons), make overhead transparencies from the blackline masters, write on transparencies placed over the pages, or use paper copies to demonstrate how to complete the lessons.

Extra Practice Lessons

CAUTION

Use these lessons only if needed. Students who need Extra Practice may benefit from one, two, or three lessons.

Student Materials

READ WELL 2 **MATERIALS (for each student, as needed)**

See Extra Practice blackline masters located on the CD.

- Unit 11 Extra Practice 1: Decoding Practice, Fluency Passage, Word Fluency A, and Activity
- Unit 11 Extra Practice 2: Decoding Practice, Fluency Passage, Word Fluency B, and Activity
- Unit 11 Extra Practice 3: Decoding Practice, Fluency Passage, Word Fluency A or B, and Activity

SCHOOL SUPPLIES

Pencils, colors (markers, crayons, or colored pencils), highlighters

Important Tips

Multisyllabic Word Fluency

"Many big words occur infrequently, but when they do occur, they carry much of the meaning and content of what is being read . . . " (Cunningham, 1998, p. 189).

Your students are well on their way to reading widely for enjoyment and learning.

In the remaining units of *Read Well 2* and *Read Well 2 Plus*, students continue to review letter/sound associations for maintenance and automaticity but also focus on reading many multisyllabic words. Your students will practice the strategy good readers use when they encounter big words they do not know. Try reading the following word and think about what you do:

bellactopleximosis

As good readers do, your students will continue to read big words from left to right, chunking common letter patterns, and then, when possible, using their English oral language skills to pronounce words correctly.

Once accurate, multisyllabic word fluency is the next hurdle for some students to overcome, first in lists, then in passage reading.

ACCURACY FIRST, THEN FLUENCY

Follow the procedures for teaching the exercises. These procedures systematically reinforce the strategy of chunking syllables from left to right.

- Have students read the words by parts.
- Have students read the whole word.
- Gently correct errors and have students reread.
- Return to difficult words for three correct responses.
- Reread the column or row until students are 100% accurate.
- Reread, mixing group and individual turns, to build fluency.

REREAD EXERCISE TASKS FOR FLUENCY

On each multisyllabic word, word ending, or affix list, have students work on fluency once accuracy has been established.

- Have students chorally read the column.
  Say something like:
  Let's practice for fluency.
  Set a pace. Read about this fast: difference, tattoos, undisturbed, master . . .
  Your turn. (difference, tattoos, undisturbed . . .)
  Have students repeat words that may be difficult.
  The word *undisturbed* is a mouthful.
  Listen: undisturbed.
  Say it two times.
  (undisturbed, undisturbed)
  While I was gone, no one touched my food.
  It was . . . undisturbed.
  Now read each word two times. Let that word *undisturbed* roll off your tongue.
  (difference, difference; tattoos, tattoos; undisturbed, undisturbed . . .)

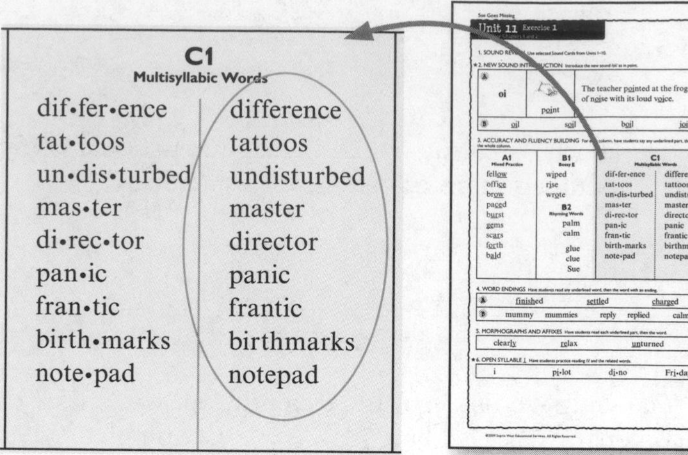

From Unit 11, Exercise 1

INCLUDE EXTRA PRACTICE WORD FLUENCY READING

If a student or students need more practice, include daily repeated readings of Rhyming and Related Words from the Extra Practice Word Fluencies.

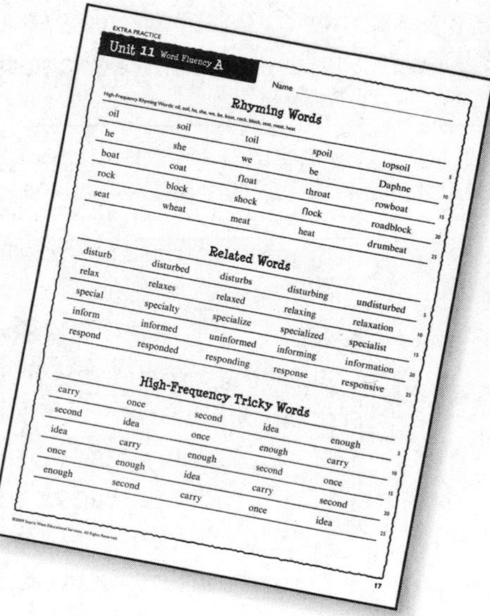

DURING STORY READING

If students tend to stall when they encounter multisyllabic words during Story Reading, remind them to use their part-by-part strategy. Say something like:

If you see a big word that might be difficult, remember to use your strategy. Get the word started by saying the parts. Don't stop.

If a student stalls during Story Reading, don't wait. Gently start the part-by-part reading. If the sentence is "We saw a hadrosaurus running back to its nest," your assistance might be as follows:

(We saw a . . .) had . . . (hadrosaurus running back to its nest.)

In this example, you would help with just the first syllable. After the Story Reading, put any difficult words on the board and have students practice for accuracy and fluency. You may wish to periodically write a difficult sentence on the board and have students practice for accuracy and fluency.

How to Teach the Lessons

Teach from this section. Each instructional component is outlined in an easy-to-teach format.

Exercise 1

- Unit and Story Opener: Dog Detective, Sue Goes Missing
- Vocabulary
- Story Reading 1
  With the Teacher: Chapter 1
  On Your Own: Chapter 2
- Comprehension and Skill Activities 1, 2

Exercise 2a

- Exercise 2b: Focus Lesson
- Story Reading 2
  With the Teacher: Chapter 3
  On Your Own: Chapter 4
- Comprehension and Skill Activities 3, 4

Exercise 3a

- Exercise 3b: Focus Lesson
- Story Reading 3
  With the Teacher: Chapter 5
  On Your Own: Chapter 6
- Comprehension and Skill Activities 5, 6

Exercise 4

- Story Reading 4
  With the Teacher: Chapter 7
- Comprehension and Skill Activities 7, 8

Exercise 5

- Story Reading 5
  With the Teacher: Dog Detective Succeeds (Fluency)
- Comprehension and Skill Activity 9a, 9b

Exercise 6

- Story Reading 6
  With the Teacher: Sue: The Real Story (Fluency)
- Written Assessment

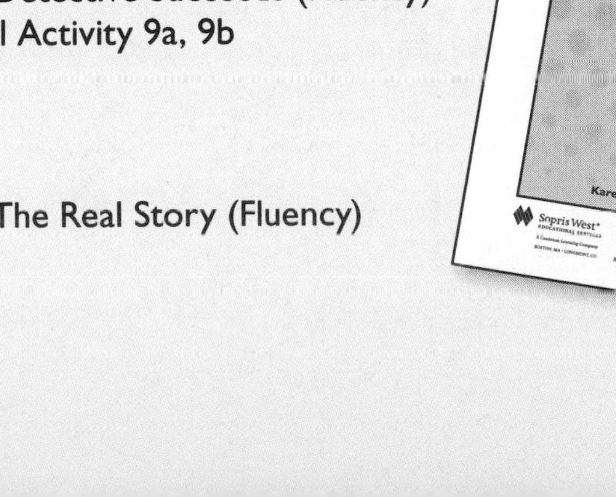

Note: Lessons include daily homework.

❶ SOUND REVIEW

Use selected Sound Cards from Units 1–10.

PACING

Exercise 1 should take about 15 minutes.

★❷ NEW SOUND INTRODUCTION

- For Row A, tell students they will learn the sound for o-i.
  Say something like:
  Look at the picture. Say "o-i says /oi/ as in point." (o-i says /oi/ as in point.)
  Read the sentence. (The teacher pointed at the frog that was making lots of noise with its loud voice.)
  Which three words have the /oi/ sound? (pointed, noise, voice)
- For Row B, have students read the underlined sound, then the word.
- After reading the row, have students go back and read the whole words.

❸ ACCURACY AND FLUENCY BUILDING

- For each task, have students say any underlined part, then read the word.
- Set a pace. Then have students read the whole words in each task and column.
- Provide repeated practice, building accuracy first, then fluency.

C1. Multisyllabic Words

- For the list of words divided by syllables, have students read each syllable, then the whole word. Use the word in a sentence, as appropriate.
- For the list of whole words, build accuracy and then fluency.

difference Frogs and toads are not the same. What is the . . . *difference?*
tattoos Look at that man's arms. He has a lot of . . . *tattoos.*
undisturbed The fossils had been left . . . *undisturbed.*
master He is an expert piano player. He is a . . . *master.*
director The person in charge of a museum is the . . . *director.*
panic When the lights went out, my sister started to . . . *panic.*
frantic Mom couldn't find her wallet and was . . . *frantic.*
birthmarks These are marks I had when I was born. They are . . . *birthmarks.*
notepad Mason took notes on a . . . *notepad.*

D1. Tricky Words

- For each Tricky Word, have students use the sounds and word parts they know to silently sound out the word. Use the word in a sentence to help with pronunciation.
- If the word is unfamiliar, tell students the word.

figured
Look at the first word. Sound the word out silently. Thumbs up when you know the word.
Use my sentence to help you pronounce the word. That's just what I . . . *figured.*
Read the word three times. (figured, figured, figured)

listening He didn't understand the lesson because he wasn't . . . *listening.*
specialty I love to cook. Spaghetti and meatballs is my . . . *specialty.*
solves The smart detective . . . *solves* . . . mysteries.

- Have students go back and read the whole words in the column.

❹ WORD ENDINGS

❺ MORPHOGRAPHS AND AFFIXES

★= New in this unit

★ 6 OPEN SYLLABLE I

- Tell students that the i in each of these words says its name.
- Have students read the underlined sound, then the whole word.

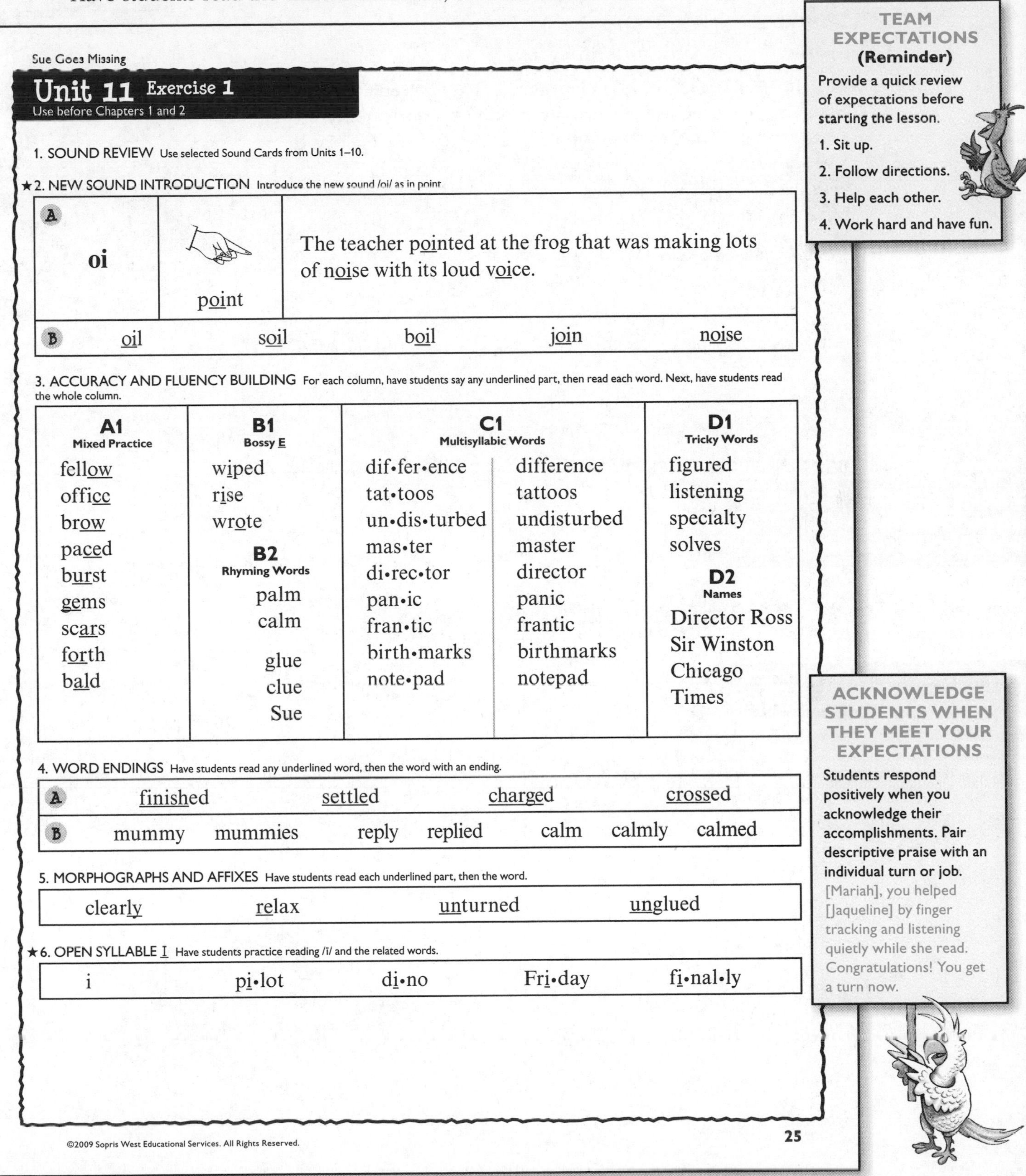

Sue Goes Missing

Unit 11 Exercise 1
Use before Chapters 1 and 2

1. SOUND REVIEW Use selected Sound Cards from Units 1–10.

★2. NEW SOUND INTRODUCTION Introduce the new sound /oi/ as in point.

A oi	point	The teacher pointed at the frog that was making lots of noise with its loud voice.

B oil soil boil join noise

3. ACCURACY AND FLUENCY BUILDING For each column, have students say any underlined part, then read each word. Next, have students read the whole column.

A1 Mixed Practice	B1 Bossy E	C1 Multisyllabic Words		D1 Tricky Words
fellow	wiped	dif•fer•ence	difference	figured
office	rise	tat•toos	tattoos	listening
brow	wrote	un•dis•turbed	undisturbed	specialty
paced	**B2** Rhyming Words	mas•ter	master	solves
burst		di•rec•tor	director	**D2** Names
gems	palm	pan•ic	panic	Director Ross
scars	calm	fran•tic	frantic	Sir Winston
forth	glue	birth•marks	birthmarks	Chicago
bald	clue	note•pad	notepad	Times
	Sue			

4. WORD ENDINGS Have students read any underlined word, then the word with an ending.

A finished settled charged crossed

B mummy mummies reply replied calm calmly calmed

5. MORPHOGRAPHS AND AFFIXES Have students read each underlined part, then the word.

clearly relax unturned unglued

★6. OPEN SYLLABLE I Have students practice reading /ī/ and the related words.

i pi•lot di•no Fri•day fi•nal•ly

25

TEAM EXPECTATIONS (Reminder)

Provide a quick review of expectations before starting the lesson.

1. Sit up.
2. Follow directions.
3. Help each other.
4. Work hard and have fun.

ACKNOWLEDGE STUDENTS WHEN THEY MEET YOUR EXPECTATIONS

Students respond positively when you acknowledge their accomplishments. Pair descriptive praise with an individual turn or job.

[Mariah], you helped [Jaqueline] by finger tracking and listening quietly while she read. Congratulations! You get a turn now.

COMPREHENSION PROCESSES

Remember, Understand, Apply

PROCEDURES

1. Introducing the Unit and Story

Using the Table of Contents; Identifying—Titles; Predicting; Inferring; Classifying—Genre; Using Vocabulary—imagination

- Have students identify the title of their new unit and story. Say something like:

  Find the Table of Contents.
  Now find Unit 11.

  What's the title of Unit 11? (Dog Detective)
  What do you think this unit will be about?
  (It will be about a dog detective.)

  What do you think a dog detective is doing in a book about dinosaurs?
  (The dog will look for dinosaur bones. The dog will find a missing dinosaur . . .)
  Those are all great predictions.

  Find the name of the story in this unit.
  What's the title? (Sue Goes Missing)

- Discuss the genre.

  Your Table of Contents also tells what kind of story you are going to read. Look under the title "Sue Goes Missing."
  What kind of story is this?
  (Fiction, Imaginative)

  That's right. What does the word *fiction* tell you? (It's a made-up story.)

  What does the word *imaginative* mean? (Someone used his or her imagination to write the story.)

  Exactly. Now find the title page for "Sue Goes Missing." What page should we turn to? (page 55)

TABLE OF CONTENTS

UNIT 11 • Dog Detective

4

2. Introducing the Title Page

Identifying—Title, Author; Inferring; Making Connections

- Have students look at the title page. Introduce the author and the topic.

  Everyone, turn to page 55. What's the title of this story? (Sue Goes Missing)

  Who used her imagination to write the story? (Marilyn Sprick)

  Who is Marilyn Sprick? (She is the author.)

  Marilyn Sprick also helped write "Sir Henry." "Sir Henry" and "Sue Goes Missing" are stories that were inspired by two real dogs. The dog detective in this story is Sir Winston.

  The real Sir Winston lives in Hawaii. Who do you think he lives with? (Sir Henry and John White)

  Yes, Sir Winston is Sir Henry's brother.

  The author has written many stories. This story is one of her favorites. As you are reading, see if you can figure out why the author likes this story.

- Discuss the gray text questions under the picture.

Sue Goes Missing

by Marilyn Sprick
illustrated by Janet Pederson

Look at the picture on page 54. This shows the real Sir Winston. Now look at Janet Pederson's illustration of Sir Winston on page 55. How does the illustration look like the real Sir Winston?[1]

55

[1] **Understand:** Viewing, Inferring (The dog in the illustration is brown and white like the real Sir Winston. They're both wearing hats . . .)

COMPREHENSION PROCESSES

Understand, Apply

PROCEDURES

Introducing Vocabulary

★**frantic** ★**undisturbed** ★**specialty** ★**come unglued**

- For each vocabulary word, have students read the word by parts, then read the whole word.
- Read the student-friendly explanations to students as they follow with their fingers. Then have students use the vocabulary word by following the gray text.
- Review and discuss the photos.

★ = New in this unit

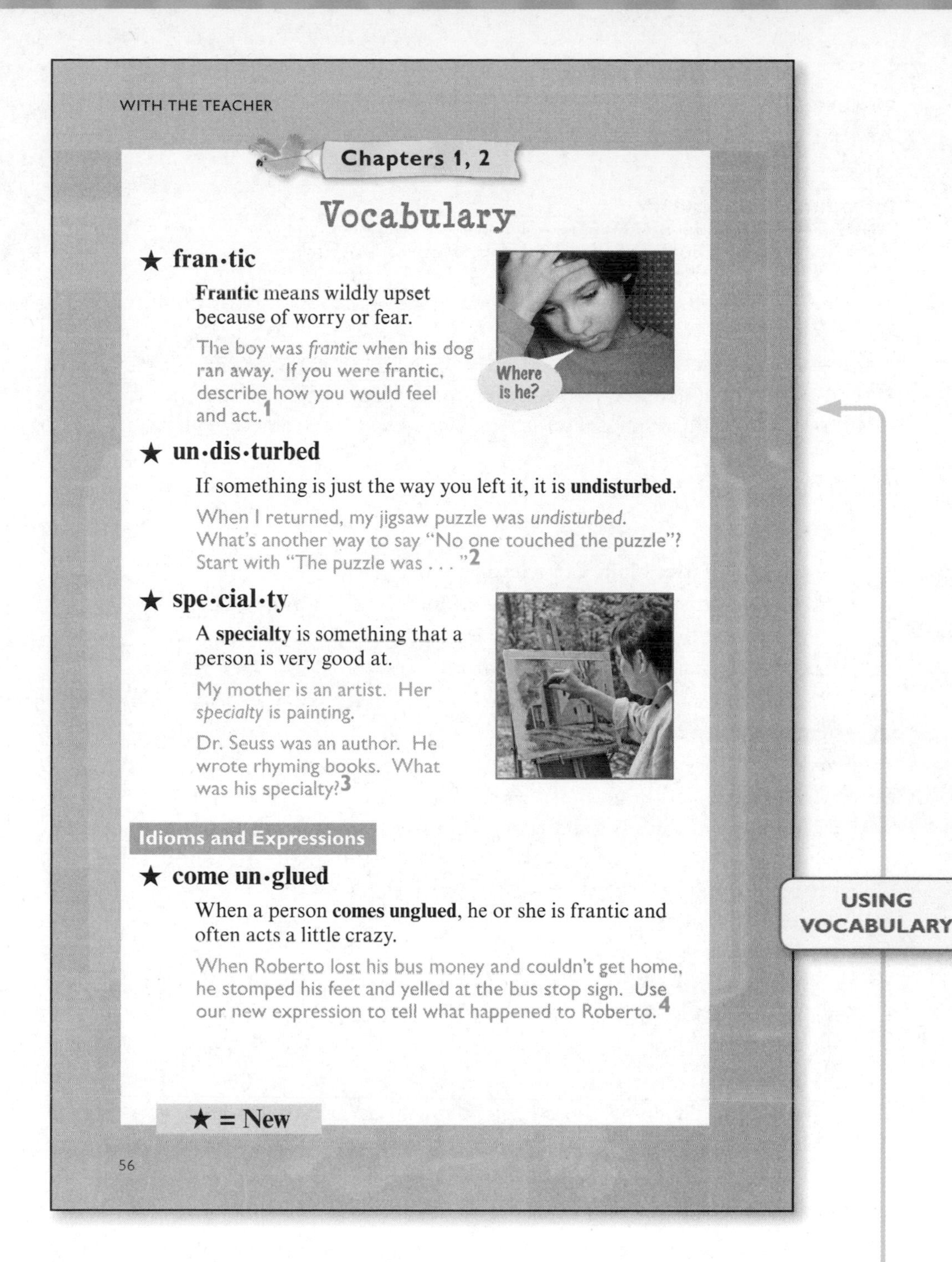

WITH THE TEACHER

Chapters 1, 2

Vocabulary

★ **fran·tic**

Frantic means wildly upset because of worry or fear.

The boy was *frantic* when his dog ran away. If you were frantic, describe how you would feel and act.[1]

★ **un·dis·turbed**

If something is just the way you left it, it is **undisturbed**.

When I returned, my jigsaw puzzle was *undisturbed*. What's another way to say "No one touched the puzzle"? Start with "The puzzle was . . . "[2]

★ **spe·cial·ty**

A **specialty** is something that a person is very good at.

My mother is an artist. Her *specialty* is painting.

Dr. Seuss was an author. He wrote rhyming books. What was his specialty?[3]

Idioms and Expressions

★ **come un·glued**

When a person **comes unglued**, he or she is frantic and often acts a little crazy.

When Roberto lost his bus money and couldn't get home, he stomped his feet and yelled at the bus stop sign. Use our new expression to tell what happened to Roberto.[4]

★ = New

56

USING VOCABULARY

1. **Apply:** Making Connections; **Understand:** Describing; Defining and Using Vocabulary—frantic (If I were frantic, I would be upset and act a little crazy.)
2. **Understand:** Using Vocabulary—undisturbed (The puzzle was undisturbed.)
3. **Understand:** Using Vocabulary—specialty (Dr. Seuss' specialty was writing rhyming books.)
4. **Apply:** Using Idioms and Expressions—come unglued (Roberto came unglued.)

CHAPTER 1 INSTRUCTIONS

Students read Chapter 1 with the teacher and Chapter 2 on their own.
Note: If you're working on an 8- to 11-Day Plan, you will read Chapter 2 with students.

COMPREHENSION PROCESSES

Remember, Understand, Apply

COMPREHENSION BUILDING

- Encourage students to answer questions with complete sentences.
- If students have difficulty comprehending, think aloud with them or reread the portion of the story that answers the question. Then repeat the question.

PROCEDURES

1. Introducing Chapter 1

Identifying—Title, Main Character

- Have students read the title and identify the main character.
  What's the title of the chapter? (An Ordinary Day)
  Look at the picture. Who is the main character? (Sir Winston)

2. First Reading

- Ask questions and discuss the story as indicated by the gray text.
- Mix group and individual turns, independent of your voice.
  Have students work toward a group accuracy goal of 0–5 errors.
  Quietly keep track of errors made by all students in the group.
- After reading the story, practice any difficult words.
  Reread the story if students have not reached the accuracy goal.

3. Second Reading, Short Passage Practice: Developing Prosody

- Demonstrate expressive, fluent reading of the first paragraph.
  Read at a rate slightly faster than the students' rate. Say something like:
  Who is telling the story? (Sir Winston is telling the story.)
  That's right. Listen to me as I read the first paragraph. I'm going to pretend that I'm really Sir Winston. Remember, he is very calm and businesslike, so I'm going to read in a calm and businesslike voice. He's also a little bored in this opening chapter, so I'm going to make my voice sound flat and weary.

  "It was an ordinary Friday. Nothing much was happening. I had just finished a dusty job out of town . . . "

- Guide practice with your voice.
- Provide individual turns while others track with their fingers and whisper read.
- Repeat with one paragraph at a time. Repeat steps with each remaining paragraph.

CORRECTING DECODING ERRORS

During story reading, gently correct any error, then have students reread the sentence.

REPEATED READINGS

Prosody

On the second reading, students practice developing prosody—phrasing and expression. Research has shown that prosody is related to both fluency and comprehension.

SUE GOES MISSING

Chapter 1

An Ordinary Day

It was an ordinary Friday. Nothing much was happening. I had just finished a dusty job out of town. I'd found a colony of ants. Now I was back in the office. Tick, tick, tick . . . time was not flying by.

I wrote my brother an e-mail. I opened a bag of Hound Dog Snacks. Then I settled down to read the *Chicago Times*. Suddenly, the door burst open.

A frantic, well-dressed man charged into my office. I looked up. The poor fellow clearly had a problem. A dog detective solves problems. This man had come to the right place.

I decided to wait while the man calmed down. He paced back and forth. Finally, he sat down across my desk and wiped his brow.

Where does this story take place?[1] At the beginning of the chapter, what kind of day was it?[2] What happened to change the mood of the story?[3]

57

COMPREHENDING AS YOU GO

1. **Apply:** Inferring—Setting (This story takes place in a detective's office. It takes place in Chicago.)
2. **Remember:** Identifying—What; Using Vocabulary—ordinary (It was an ordinary day; not much was happening; time was going slow . . .)
3. **Understand:** Explaining—Event; Using Vocabulary—frantic (A frantic man came into the office.)

I gave the man a glass of water. Then I said, "If you have a problem, you've come to the right place. I'm Sir Winston, master detective. I leave no stone unturned. There is no problem too big or small for a dog detective to solve."

This seemed to make a difference. The man began to relax. "My name is Ross," he said. "I run the museum. I'm sure you've heard what happened." Then he sadly shook his head.

Having been out of town, I hadn't heard. So I said, "Please start from the beginning."

Director Ross began, "It was an ordinary day, just another Friday. As is my habit, I'd gone to the museum early. I put on the coffee, but something didn't seem right. I had a feeling that something was wrong. So I decided to take a walk through the museum.

"I walked through the museum. The gems were undisturbed, and the mummies were fine. So I thought to myself, 'It's just your imagination.'

Sir Winston is a master detective who leaves no stone unturned. What does this mean?[1]

FOCUS ON INFERENCE

Following the Clues

After completing the page, say something like: Something big is going on. Director Ross said, "I'm sure you've heard what happened."

Does Sir Winston know what happened? (no)

Why not? (He was out of town.)

What is Director Ross explaining? (He is explaining what happened.)

What do we know so far? (Director Ross thought something was wrong at the museum.)

That's right. We know something is wrong. We know that Director Ross is upset, and we know that something big is going on. Do we know anything else?

COMPREHENDING AS YOU GO

1 **Apply:** Inferring, Explaining (It means that he looks everywhere to find clues. It means he doesn't miss anything . . .)

COMPREHENDING AS YOU GO

❶ **Apply:** Inferring, Explaining (Someone stole something from the museum. Maybe one of the dinosaur fossils is missing . . .)

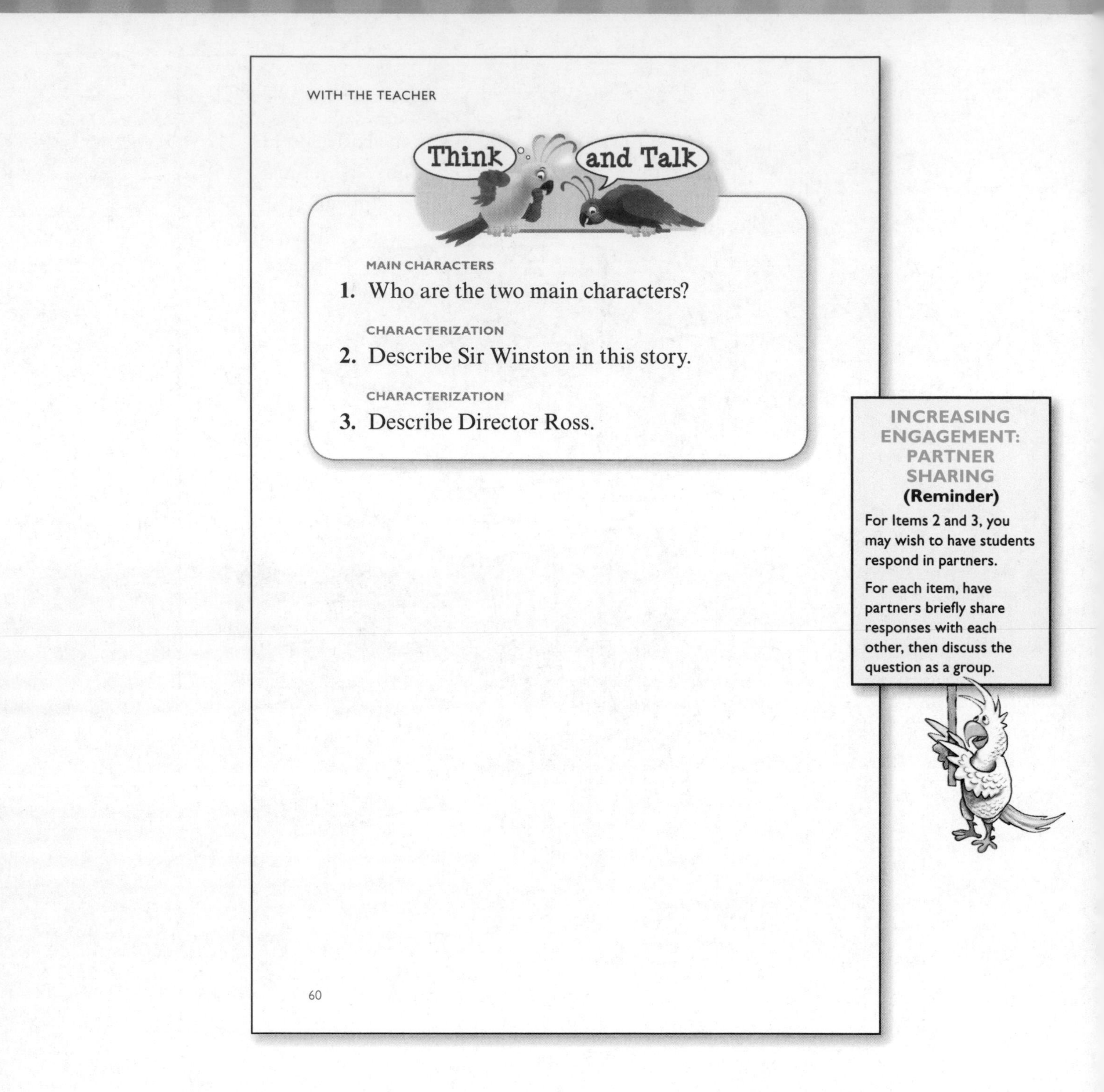

INCREASING ENGAGEMENT: PARTNER SHARING (Reminder)

For Items 2 and 3, you may wish to have students respond in partners.

For each item, have partners briefly share responses with each other, then discuss the question as a group.

1. **Remember:** Identifying—Main Characters (The main characters are Sir Winston and Director Ross.)
2. **Understand:** Describing; **Apply:** Inferring—Character Traits (Characterization) (Sir Winston is a dog detective. He is confident, calm, and patient.)
3. **Understand:** Describing; **Apply:** Inferring—Character Traits (Characterization); Using Vocabulary—frantic (Director Ross is frantic. He's having trouble telling Sir Winston what's wrong. He doesn't communicate well.)

CHAPTER 2 INSTRUCTIONS

Students read without the teacher, independently or with partners.

Note: If you're working on an 8- to 11-Day Plan, you will read Chapter 2 with your students.

PREP NOTE

Setting a Purpose

Write questions on a chalkboard, white board, or large piece of paper before working with your small group.

COMPREHENSION PROCESSES

Remember, Understand, Apply

PROCEDURES FOR READING ON YOUR OWN

1. Getting Ready

Have students turn to "Sue Goes Missing," Chapter 2, on page 61.

2. Setting a Purpose

Identifying—Problem; Describing; Explaining

Before students begin reading, say something like:

What's the title of Chapter 2? (Unglued)

We learned that Sir Winston is a dog detective and that Director Ross has a problem.

Read to find out the answers to these questions:

- What is the problem?
- What clues does Sir Winston find out about Sue?

3. Reading on Your Own: Partner or Whisper Reading

- Have students take turns reading every other page with a partner, or have students whisper read Chapter 2 on their own.
- Continue having students track each word with their fingers.
- Have students ask themselves or their partners the gray text questions.

For Whisper Reading, say something like:

Everyone, turn to page 61. This is where you're going to start reading on your own—without me. You will whisper read as you track with your finger, so I can see where you are in your work.

Ask yourself the gray text questions. Remember, you get to be your own teacher.

For Partner Reading, say something like:

Everyone, turn to page 61. This is where you're going to start Partner Reading.

Where are you going to sit? (at our desks, side by side)

You will take turns reading pages. If you are the listener, what will you do? (keep my book flat, follow with my finger, compliment my partner, ask my partner the gray text questions)

If you are the reader, what will you do? (keep my book flat, finger track, read quietly, answer questions)

4. Comprehension and Skill Work

For students on a 6-Day Plan, tell them they will do Comprehension and Skill Activities 1 and 2 after they read Chapter 2 on their own. Guide practice, as needed. For teacher directions, see pages 29 and 30. (For 8- to 11-Day Plans, see the Lesson Planner, page 9.)

5. Homework 1: Repeated Reading

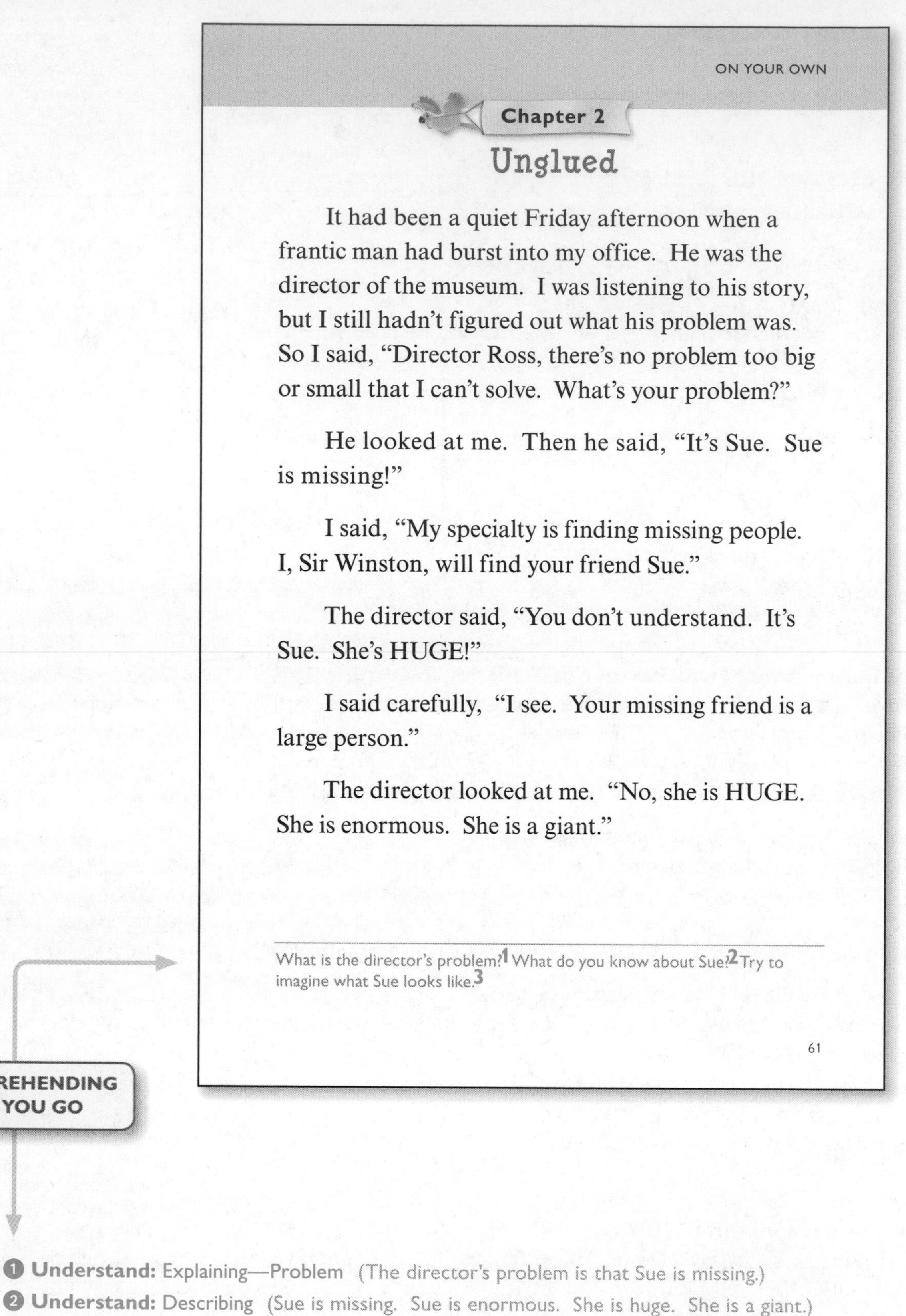

ON YOUR OWN

Chapter 2

Unglued

It had been a quiet Friday afternoon when a frantic man had burst into my office. He was the director of the museum. I was listening to his story, but I still hadn't figured out what his problem was. So I said, "Director Ross, there's no problem too big or small that I can't solve. What's your problem?"

He looked at me. Then he said, "It's Sue. Sue is missing!"

I said, "My specialty is finding missing people. I, Sir Winston, will find your friend Sue."

The director said, "You don't understand. It's Sue. She's HUGE!"

I said carefully, "I see. Your missing friend is a large person."

The director looked at me. "No, she is HUGE. She is enormous. She is a giant."

What is the director's problem?[1] What do you know about Sue?[2] Try to imagine what Sue looks like.[3]

61

COMPREHENDING AS YOU GO

❶ **Understand:** Explaining—Problem (The director's problem is that Sue is missing.)
❷ **Understand:** Describing (Sue is missing. Sue is enormous. She is huge. She is a giant.)
❸ **Apply:** Visualizing (She is ten feet tall . . .)

ON YOUR OWN

Hearing the panic rise in the director's voice, I said calmly, "I see. My first clue—the missing person is a very large woman, a very, very large woman."

The director looked at me, and then he laughed. I thought to myself, "He's coming unglued. I'd better get this Sue back fast." I pulled out my notepad. A detective always asks questions and takes notes. I asked, "Color of hair?"

What does Sir Winston know about Sue?[1] Why does Sir Winston think Director Ross is *coming unglued*?[2] What does that mean?[3]

62

COMPREHENDING AS YOU GO

1. **Understand:** Explaining (He knows that she is very, very large.)
2. **Apply:** Inferring, Explaining, Using Idioms and Expressions—come unglued (Sir Winston thinks Director Ross is coming unglued because he can hear panic in the director's voice and then the director laughed.)
3. **Apply:** Defining Idioms and Expressions—come unglued (When someone is coming unglued, he or she is frantic and acting a little crazy, just like Director Ross.)

COMPREHENDING AS YOU GO

❶ **Understand:** Viewing, Describing (She is very large, she is bald, and she has big teeth.)

STORY COMPREHENSION

COMPREHENSION PROCESSES

Remember, Understand

WRITING TRAITS

Conventions—Capital, Period, Comma, Quotation Marks
Presentation

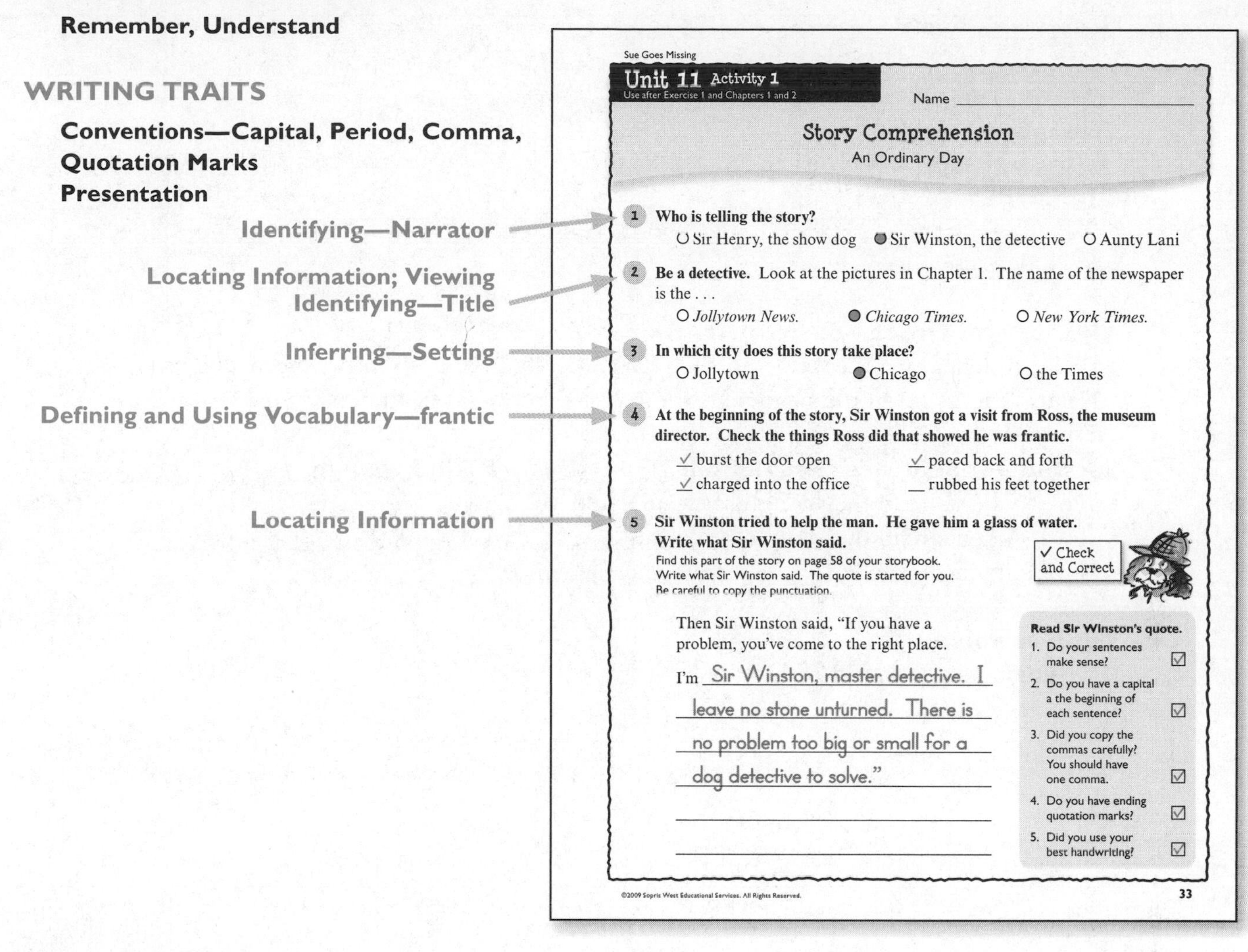

Sue Goes Missing

Unit 11 Activity 1
Use after Exercise 1 and Chapters 1 and 2

Name ____________________

Story Comprehension
An Ordinary Day

1. **Who is telling the story?**
   ○ Sir Henry, the show dog ● Sir Winston, the detective ○ Aunty Lani

2. **Be a detective.** Look at the pictures in Chapter 1. The name of the newspaper is the . . .
   ○ *Jollytown News.* ● *Chicago Times.* ○ *New York Times.*

3. **In which city does this story take place?**
   ○ Jollytown ● Chicago ○ the Times

4. **At the beginning of the story, Sir Winston got a visit from Ross, the museum director. Check the things Ross did that showed he was frantic.**
   ✓ burst the door open ✓ paced back and forth
   ✓ charged into the office _ rubbed his feet together

5. **Sir Winston tried to help the man. He gave him a glass of water. Write what Sir Winston said.**
   Find this part of the story on page 58 of your storybook. Write what Sir Winston said. The quote is started for you. Be careful to copy the punctuation.

   Then Sir Winston said, "If you have a problem, you've come to the right place.
   I'm Sir Winston, master detective. I leave no stone unturned. There is no problem too big or small for a dog detective to solve."

✓ Check and Correct

Read Sir Winston's quote.
1. Do your sentences make sense? ☑
2. Do you have a capital a the beginning of each sentence? ☑
3. Did you copy the commas carefully? You should have one comma. ☑
4. Do you have ending quotation marks? ☑
5. Did you use your best handwriting? ☑

©2009 Sopris West Educational Services. All Rights Reserved. 33

PROCEDURES

For each step, demonstrate and guide practice, as needed. Then have students complete the page independently.

1. **Selection Response—Basic Instructions** (Items 1, 2, 3)
   Have students read each question, then fill in the bubble with the correct answer.

2. **Vocabulary: Selection Response—Basic Instructions** (Item 4)
   Have students read the sentences, then check the correct responses.

3. **Quote: Locating Information—Specific Instructions** (Item 5)
   Have students read the item, locate the information in their storybook, and copy the quote.

Self-monitoring
Have students use the Check and Correct box to check and correct their work.

VOCABULARY AND ALPHABETICAL ORDER

COMPREHENSION PROCESSES

Understand, Apply

WRITING TRAITS

Conventions—Period

PROCEDURES

For each step, demonstrate and guide practice, as needed. Then have students complete the page independently.

Alphabetical Order—Basic Instructions

- Have students read the letters in the alphabet column and fill in the missing letters.
- Have students fill in the blanks for the vocabulary words in the column.

Vocabulary: Sentence Completion, Illustrating—Basic Instructions

- Have students read the vocabulary words and definitions.
- Have students read the sample sentences and fill in the blanks.
- Have students visualize and illustrate each sentence.

Self-monitoring

Have students check and correct their work.

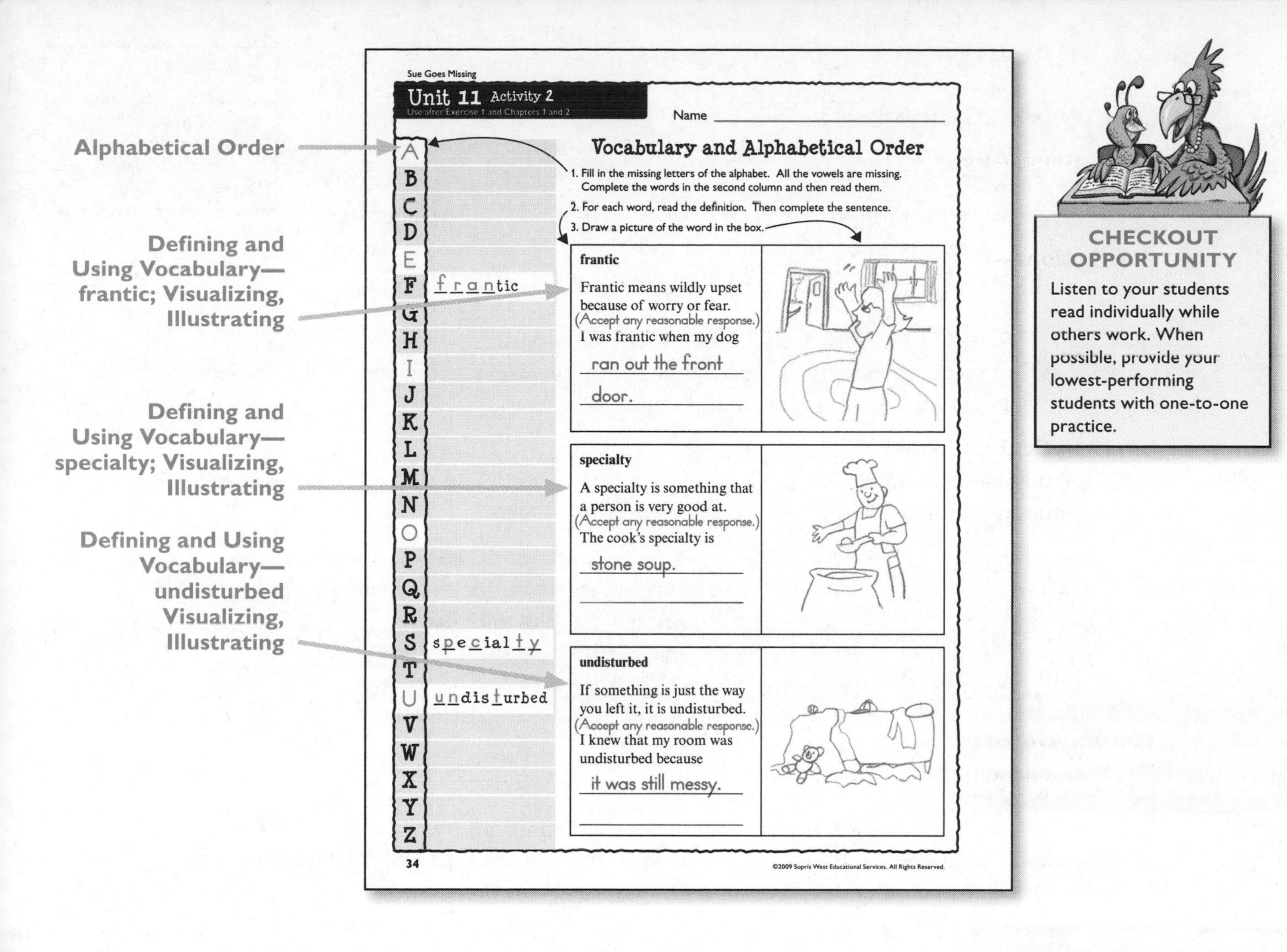

Sue Goes Missing

Unit 11 Activity 2

Use after Exercise 1 and Chapters 1 and 2

Name ______________________

Vocabulary and Alphabetical Order

1. Fill in the missing letters of the alphabet. All the vowels are missing. Complete the words in the second column and then read them.
2. For each word, read the definition. Then complete the sentence.
3. Draw a picture of the word in the box.

A B C D E F G H I J K L M N O P Q R S T U V W X Y Z

F — frantic
S — specialty
U — undisturbed

frantic

Frantic means wildly upset because of worry or fear.

(Accept any reasonable response.)

I was frantic when my dog ran out the front door.

specialty

A specialty is something that a person is very good at.

(Accept any reasonable response.)

The cook's specialty is stone soup.

undisturbed

If something is just the way you left it, it is undisturbed.

(Accept any reasonable response.)

I knew that my room was undisturbed because it was still messy.

34

Alphabetical Order

Defining and Using Vocabulary—frantic; Visualizing, Illustrating

Defining and Using Vocabulary—specialty; Visualizing, Illustrating

Defining and Using Vocabulary—undisturbed Visualizing, Illustrating

CHECKOUT OPPORTUNITY

Listen to your students read individually while others work. When possible, provide your lowest-performing students with one-to-one practice.

❶ SOUND REVIEW

> **PACING**
> Exercise 2a should take about 10 minutes, allowing about 10 minutes for the Main Idea and Supporting Details Focus Lesson.

❷ SHIFTY WORD BLENDING

❸ SOUND PRACTICE

- For each task, have students spell and say the focus sound in the gray bar.
- Next, have students read each underlined sound, the word, then the whole column. Repeat, building accuracy, then fluency.

❹ ACCURACY AND FLUENCY BUILDING

For each task, have students say any underlined part, then read the whole word. Provide repeated practice, building accuracy first, then fluency.

C1. Multisyllabic Words

Have students read each syllable, then the whole word. Use the word in a sentence. For the list of whole words, build accuracy and then fluency.

specific I still don't know how to get to your house. Can you be more . . . *specific?*
responded We needed help, and we're happy that the community . . . *responded.*
cameras The students took many pictures with their . . . *cameras.*
photographers People who take pictures are called . . . *photographers.*
microphone Jill got on stage and sang into the . . . *microphone.*
nervous Jill was going to sing on stage for the first time. She was . . . *nervous.*
wacko Someone who is crazy is . . . *wacko.*

D1. Tricky Words

- For each Tricky Word, have students use the sounds and word parts they know to silently sound out the word. Use the word in a sentence to help with pronunciation.
- If the word is unfamiliar, tell students the word.

guy
Look at the first word. This word rhymes with *buy*. Read the word. (guy)
A man is sometimes called a . . . *guy.*
Read the word three times. (guy, guy, guy)

shoved
Look at the next word. Sound out the word silently. Thumbs up when you know the word.
The big rock was hard to move. We pushed and . . . *shoved* . . . it.
Read the word three times. (shoved, shoved, shoved)

serious
Only the first part of the next word is tricky. It says *sear.*
Say the word parts with me. ser-i-ous Amy was not joking. She was very . . . *serious.*
Read the word two times. (serious, serious)

reviewed Winston reread his notes. He . . . *reviewed* . . . them.
shoulders He didn't know so he just shrugged his . . . *shoulders.*
course The players had to run an obstacle . . . *course.*

- Have students go back and read the whole words in the column.

❺ WORD ENDINGS

❻ MORPHOGRAPHS AND AFFIXES

Sue Goes Missing

Unit 11 Exercise 2a

Use before Chapters 3 and 4

1. SOUND REVIEW Have students review sounds for accuracy, then for fluency.

A	o_e as in bone	u_e as in flute	ge as in page	igh as in flight	ow as in cow
B	ci	-dge	ce	ai	ir

2. SHIFTY WORD BLENDING For each word, have students say the underlined part, sound out smoothly, then read the word.

blues	clues	claws	jaws	paws

3. SOUND PRACTICE In each column, have students spell and say the sound, then say any underlined sound and the word. Next, have students read the whole column.

oi	kn	ph	oa	Mixed Practice
coil	known	paragraph	throat	awhile
voice	knot	phrase	road	faces
spoil	knew	photograph	boat	sweat

4. ACCURACY AND FLUENCY BUILDING For each column, have students say any underlined part, then read each word. Next, have students read the whole column.

A1 Mixed Practice	B1 Contractions	C1 Multisyllabic Words		D1 Tricky Words
age	she will	spe•cif•ic	specific	guy
broke	she'll	re•spond•ed	responded	shoved
hurt		cam•er•as	cameras	serious
large	I would	pho•tog•ra•phers	photographers	reviewed
lights	I'd	mi•cro•phone	microphone	shoulders
		ner•vous	nervous	course
		wack•o	wacko	

5. WORD ENDINGS Have students read the underlined word, then the word with an ending.

A	stormed	flashed	rubbed
B	swarmed	millions	taken

6. MORPHOGRAPHS AND AFFIXES Have students read each underlined word part, then the word.

A	vacation	information	commotion	station
B	describe	reporters	lovable	unreal

BUILDING MASTERY (Reminder)

For each task, have students work first on accuracy and then on fluency. Have fun! Practice words multiple times in varied ways. Have students whisper the words, squeak the words, and read the sounds and words in a rhythm.

GENTLE CORRECTIONS

If you hear an error, write the word on the board.

Have all students identify the difficult sound and then blend the word.

Periodically, repeat practice of the difficult word.

MAIN IDEA AND SUPPORTING DETAILS

FOCUS LESSON
Skills and Strategies

PREP NOTES

To demonstrate how to write the main idea and supporting details, use an overhead of page 27 in student *Exercise Book 2*, write on a transparency placed over the page, or use a paper copy.

PURPOSE

This lesson provides explicit instruction in identifying the main idea of a paragraph. The lesson prepares students for Comprehension and Skill Work. Students do not write in their books but will watch and respond as you guide them through the lesson.

COMPREHENSION PROCESSES

Remember, Understand

PROCEDURES

1 INTRODUCTION

Identifying—What

Demonstrate and guide the process of using supporting details to figure out and write the main idea. Say something like:

We're going to work on a *strategy*, or a way to figure out the main idea of paragraphs.

The main idea tells two things. First, a main idea tells who or what the paragraph is about. What does the main idea tell us? (It tells who or what the paragraph is about.)

Then the main idea tells the most important thing that is happening or the most important thought. What else does the main idea tell us?

(It tells the most important thing that is happening or the most important thought.)

2 MAIN IDEA AND SUPPORTING DETAILS

Identifying—Topic, Main Idea, Supporting Details; Classifying

- Have students read the paragraph, then identify the topic for Item 1.
- Have students identify three supporting details to complete Item 2.

  Item 2 tells us to list the supporting details. The supporting details are facts or small pieces of information that tell us about a dog detective. We're going to list three details.

  Look at the first box. We learned that to solve a case, a dog detective must ask . . . questions.
  Great. I'll write that in the first box. **After "ask," write "questions" in the first box.**

  Look at the next box. The paragraph told us that to solve a case, a dog detective must also *take* something. Look back at the paragraph. Touch your nose when you know what a dog detective must *take*.
  What must a dog detective take? (good notes) **After "take," write "good notes."**

  Repeat with the third box and "think clearly."

- Next, have students use the supporting details to figure out a main idea.
  Look at my paper. This is a bracket. **Point to the bracket.**
  It shows that all the details go together to form the main idea.
  What are all the details about? (a dog detective) **Write "A dog detective" on the line.**

  Let's find which statement is a good main idea for this paragraph.
  Read the topic and first choice. (A dog detective . . . must ask questions to solve a case.)
  Is that true? (yes) But it just restates a detail. It doesn't tell us about all three details.

  Read the second choice. (A dog detective . . . must work hard to solve a case.)
  Is that true? (yes) Do all three choices tell us a dog detective works hard? (yes)

Read the third choice. A dog detective . . . (must bark to solve a case).
Is that true? (maybe) The paragraph didn't tell us that detail.
Read the best choice for main idea. (A dog detective must work hard to solve a case.)

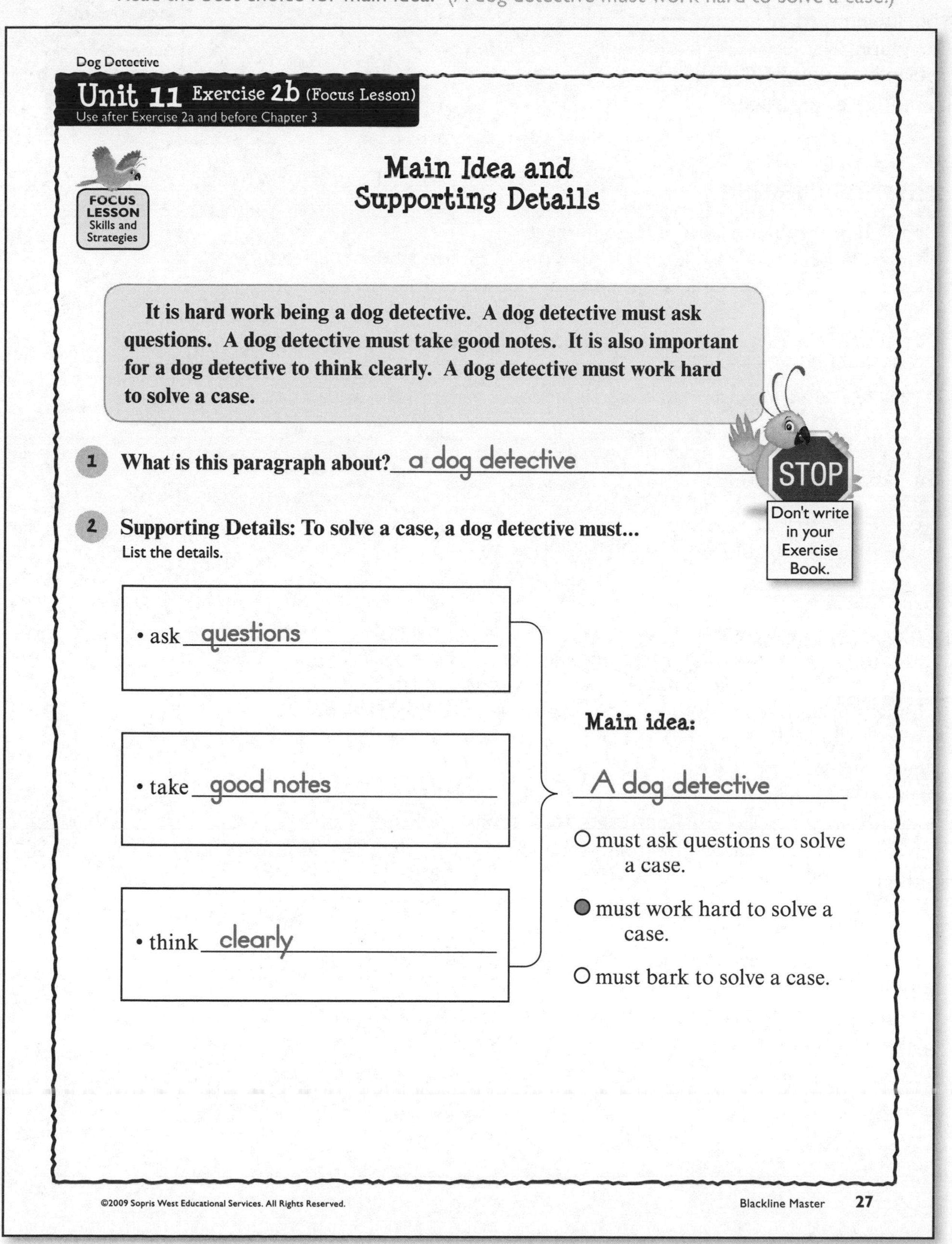
Dog Detective

Unit 11 Exercise 2b (Focus Lesson)
Use after Exercise 2a and before Chapter 3

FOCUS LESSON
Skills and Strategies

Main Idea and Supporting Details

It is hard work being a dog detective. A dog detective must ask questions. A dog detective must take good notes. It is also important for a dog detective to think clearly. A dog detective must work hard to solve a case.

1. **What is this paragraph about?** a dog detective

2. **Supporting Details: To solve a case, a dog detective must...**
List the details.

- ask questions
- take good notes
- think clearly

Main idea:

A dog detective

- ○ must ask questions to solve a case.
- ● must work hard to solve a case.
- ○ must bark to solve a case.

Blackline Master 27

CHAPTER 3 INSTRUCTIONS

Students read Chapter 3 with the teacher and Chapter 4 on their own.
Note: If you're working on an 8- to 11-Day Plan, you will read Chapter 4 with students.

COMPREHENSION PROCESSES

Understand, Apply, Analyze

PROCEDURES

1. Reviewing Chapter 2

Identifying—Problem; Describing; Inferring

- Have students turn to page 61. If time permits, have students reread Chapter 2 with you. Quickly discuss the questions from Chapter 2, Setting a Purpose. Say something like:

  Yesterday, you read Chapter 2 on your own. Let's see what you found out.

  What is the problem? (Sue is missing.)

  What does Sue look like? (She is a big lady. She is huge. She has no hair. She has big teeth.)

2. Introducing Chapter 3

Identifying—Title

Have students turn to page 64 and identify the title.

3. First Reading

- Ask questions and discuss the story as indicated by the gray text.
- Mix group and individual turns, independent of your voice.
  Have students work toward a group accuracy goal of 0–3 errors.
  Quietly keep track of errors made by all students in the group.
- After reading the story, practice any difficult words. Reread the story if students have not reached the accuracy goal.

4. Second Reading, Timed Readings: Repeated Reading

- As time allows, have students do Timed Readings while others follow along.
- Time individuals for 30 seconds and encourage each child to work for a personal best.
- Count the number of words read correctly in 30 seconds (words read minus errors).
- Multiply by two to determine words correct per minute. Record student scores.

WITH THE TEACHER

Chapter 3

Can You Help or Not?

It had taken awhile, but I had three clues about the missing Sue. She was very, very large. She was bald, and she had big teeth. It felt like I was still missing information, so I asked, "Age?"

Director Ross rubbed his head and said, "Oh, she's ancient."

I looked at him and thought, "Strange answer." I asked, "Could you be more specific?"

The director said, "She's millions and millions of years old."

Next to age, I wrote "very old." Then I scratched it out and wrote "ancient." I asked, "Okay, now. How tall is this Sue?"

How is Sir Winston learning about Sue?[1] What does Sir Winston think Sue is?[2] What has he learned so far?[3]

64

FOCUS ON INFERENCE

After completing the page, say something like:
Have you figured out who Sue is?

If appropriate, ask:
What makes you think Sue is a dinosaur? (She's millions and millions of years old!)

Does the book say Sue is a dinosaur? (no)

If you are right, you've read between the lines. You're a better detective than Sir Winston!

❶ **Understand:** Explaining (He is asking Director Ross questions.)

❷ **Apply:** Inferring (Sir Winston thinks Sue is a lady.)

❸ **Understand:** Describing; Using Vocabulary—ancient (Sue is very, very large. She is bald and has big teeth. She is ancient. She is millions and millions of years old.)

The director responded, "Just her head is five feet tall."

By now I was thinking, "This guy is really wacko." So I said, "Ross, I'm not so sure I can help you. This Sue . . . maybe she's just gone on a little vacation."

Ross looked at me. "Really," I said. "Maybe if you wait a day, she'll come back."

At that, Ross got upset again. "What?" he stormed. "You said you could solve any problem, big or small!"

Just then the door burst open again. Reporters from the *Chicago Times* were all over the place. Lights flashed. Cameras rolled, and a microphone was shoved in front of me.

FOCUS ON INFERENCE

After completing the page, say something like:
What does Sir Winston think about Director Ross? (He thinks he is wacko—crazy.)

Why does Winston think Director Ross is crazy? (Ross said that Sue's head was five feet tall.)

That's right. Can you imagine a person having a *head* as tall as this.
Show students how high five feet is.

Sir Winston still thinks Sue is a . . . person.

That's right. So, thinking someone has a head that is five feet tall would be crazy.

Something big is going on! How can you tell? (Reporters have burst into Sir Winston's office.)

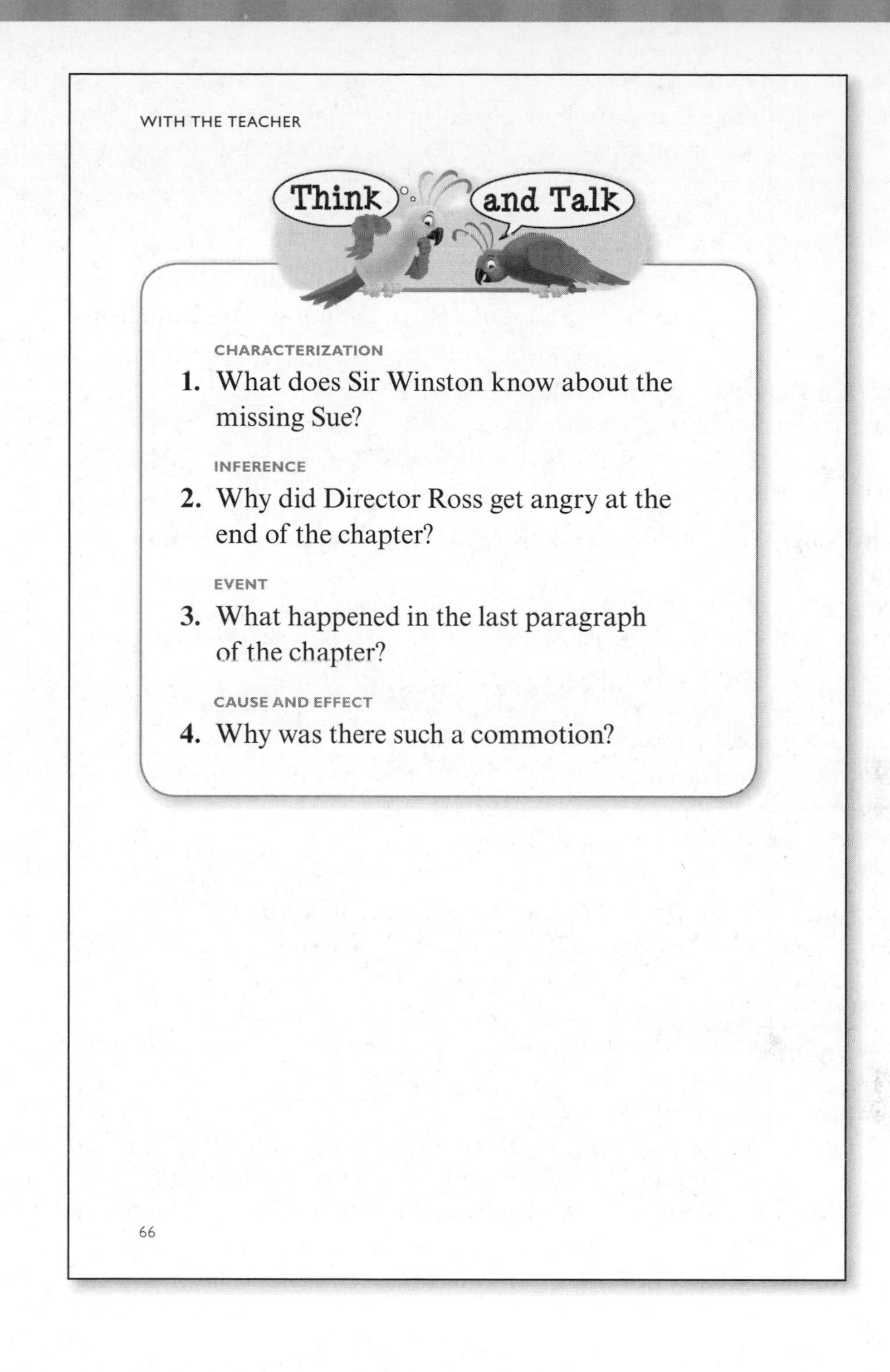

1. **Understand:** Describing—Character Traits (Characterization); Using Vocabulary—ancient (She is huge, bald, ancient, and has big teeth.)
2. **Apply:** Inferring, Explaining (He thought Sir Winston wasn't going to help him find Sue.)
3. **Understand:** Explaining (Reporters burst in. Lights flashed and cameras rolled.)
4. **Analyze:** Distinguishing Cause/Effect; Using Vocabulary—commotion (The reporters knew that Sue was missing, and Sir Winston was going to look for her, so they wanted to interview him.)

> **PREP NOTE**
> **Setting a Purpose**
> Write questions on a chalkboard, white board, or large piece of paper before working with your small group.

CHAPTER 4 INSTRUCTIONS

Students read without the teacher, independently or with partners.
Note: If you're working on an 8- to 11-Day Plan, you will read Chapter 4 with students.

COMPREHENSION PROCESSES

Remember, Understand, Apply, Evaluate

PROCEDURES

1. Getting Ready

Have students turn to Chapter 4 on page 67.

2. Setting a Purpose

Identifying—Title; Inferring; Using Vocabulary—frantic, commotion; Explaining

Before students begin reading, say something like:
Look at page 67. What's the chapter title? (No Case Too Big)
Do you think this is a big case? (yes)
Why? (Director Ross is frantic. The reporters are causing a commotion.)
Read to find out the answers to these questions:

- Who or what is missing?
- Why does Sir Winston get nervous?
- What does Sir Winston decide he can do?

3. Reading on Your Own: Partner or Whisper Reading

- Have students take turns reading every other page with a partner, or have students whisper read pages 67–69 on their own.
- Continue having students track each word with their fingers.
- Have students ask themselves or their partners the gray text questions.

4. Comprehension and Skill Work

For students on a 6-Day Plan, tell them they will do Comprehension and Skill Activities 3 and 4 after they read on their own. Guide practice, as needed. For teacher directions, see pages 44 and 45. (For 8- to 11-Day Plans, see the Lesson Planner, page 9.)

5. Homework 2: Repeated Reading

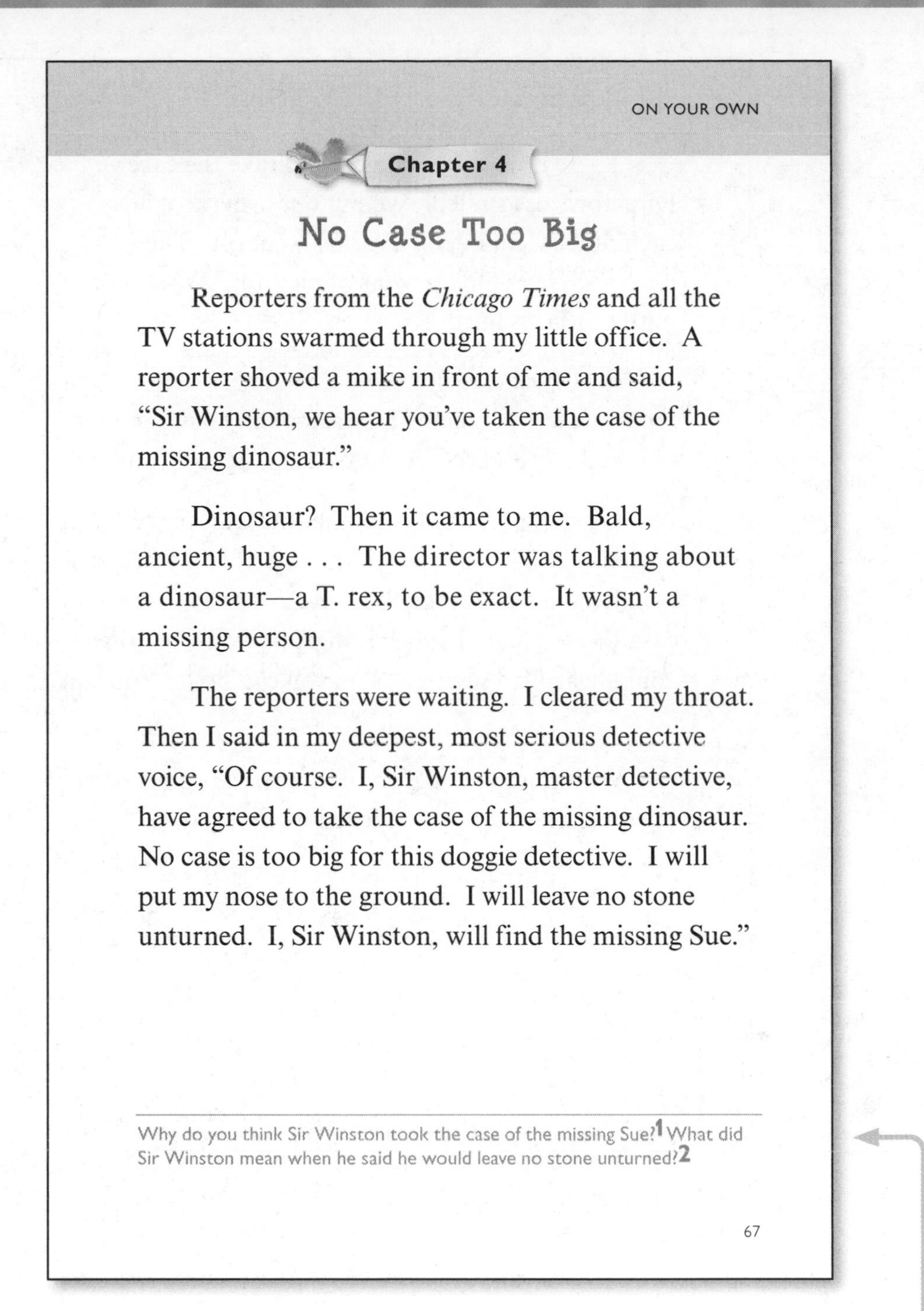

Chapter 4

No Case Too Big

Reporters from the *Chicago Times* and all the TV stations swarmed through my little office. A reporter shoved a mike in front of me and said, "Sir Winston, we hear you've taken the case of the missing dinosaur."

Dinosaur? Then it came to me. Bald, ancient, huge . . . The director was talking about a dinosaur—a T. rex, to be exact. It wasn't a missing person.

The reporters were waiting. I cleared my throat. Then I said in my deepest, most serious detective voice, "Of course. I, Sir Winston, master detective, have agreed to take the case of the missing dinosaur. No case is too big for this doggie detective. I will put my nose to the ground. I will leave no stone unturned. I, Sir Winston, will find the missing Sue."

Why do you think Sir Winston took the case of the missing Sue?[1] What did Sir Winston mean when he said he would leave no stone unturned?[2]

COMPREHENDING AS YOU GO

1. **Apply:** Inferring, Explaining (No case is too big for Sir Winston. He wanted to help Director Ross.)
2. **Understand:** Explaining (Sir Winston meant that he will look everywhere for Sue until he finds her.)

There it was. I had agreed to take the case. Director Ross smiled. We put our arms around each other's shoulders. Flashes went off. The photographers took dozens of pictures. We smiled until our faces hurt!

Finally, the commotion died down. The reporters left. Director Ross shook my paw again, thanked me, and then went back to the museum.

I reviewed my notes. Bald dinosaur, big teeth, ancient . . . Then sweat broke out across my brow. I wondered if I could solve this case. It was the biggest case I'd ever had. I started to get nervous, but then I could hear Dad saying, "Son, you can do it. You can do it."

With that, I thought, "There is no problem too big or small that this dog detective can't solve. I can do it. I can!"

Why did Sir Winston start to get nervous?[1] Do you think Sir Winston can solve the case?[2]

COMPREHENDING AS YOU GO

1 **Understand:** Explaining (He got nervous because he didn't know if he could solve the case.)

2 **Evaluate:** Responding (I think he can solve the case because he's a great detective . . .)

SUE GOES MISSING
69

STORY COMPREHENSION

COMPREHENSION PROCESSES

Remember, Understand, Apply

WRITING TRAITS

Conventions—Capital

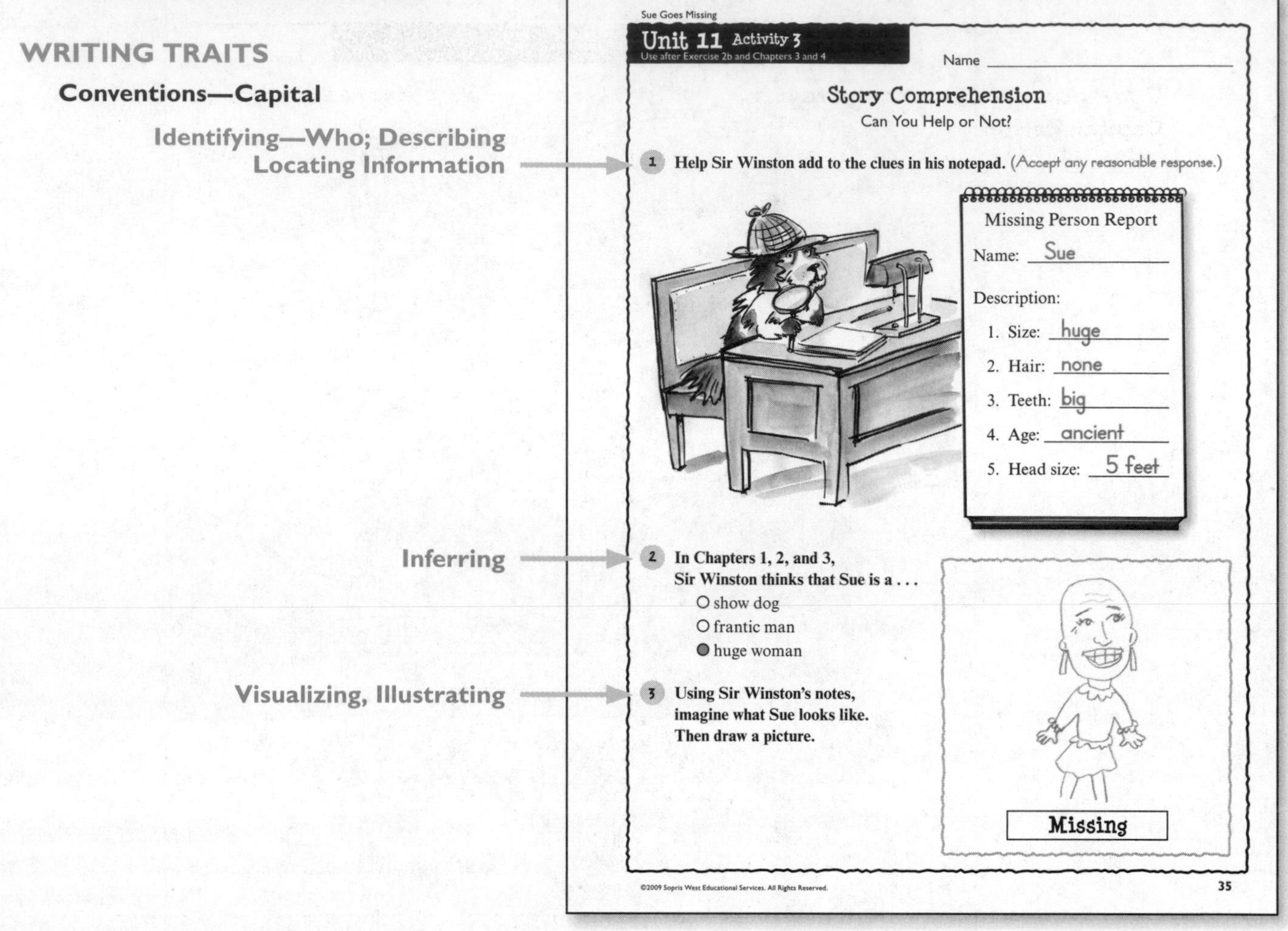
Sue Goes Missing

Unit 11 Activity 3

Use after Exercise 2b and Chapters 3 and 4

Name ____________________

Story Comprehension

Can You Help or Not?

Identifying—Who; Describing
Locating Information → 1 **Help Sir Winston add to the clues in his notepad.** (Accept any reasonable response.)

Missing Person Report

Name: Sue

Description:

1. Size: huge
2. Hair: none
3. Teeth: big
4. Age: ancient
5. Head size: 5 feet

Inferring → 2 **In Chapters 1, 2, and 3, Sir Winston thinks that Sue is a . . .**

- ○ show dog
- ○ frantic man
- ● huge woman

Visualizing, Illustrating → 3 **Using Sir Winston's notes, imagine what Sue looks like. Then draw a picture.**

35

PROCEDURES

For each step, demonstrate and guide practice, as needed. Then have students complete the page independently.

1. **Description: Note Taking—Basic Instructions** (Item 1)
   - Have students read the directions, then fill in the blanks. Remind them to look back in their storybooks if they need to.
   - Think aloud with students and discuss possible answers, as needed.

2. **Selection Response—Basic Instructions** (Item 2)
   Have students read the sentence, then fill in the bubble with the correct answer.

3. **Description: Visualizing, Illustrating—Basic Instructions** (Item 3)
   Have students read the directions, then draw an illustration in the box.

Self-monitoring

Have students check and correct their work.

MAIN IDEA AND SUPPORTING DETAILS

COMPREHENSION PROCESSES

Remember, Understand, Apply

WRITING TRAITS

Conventions—Complete Sentence, Capital, Period

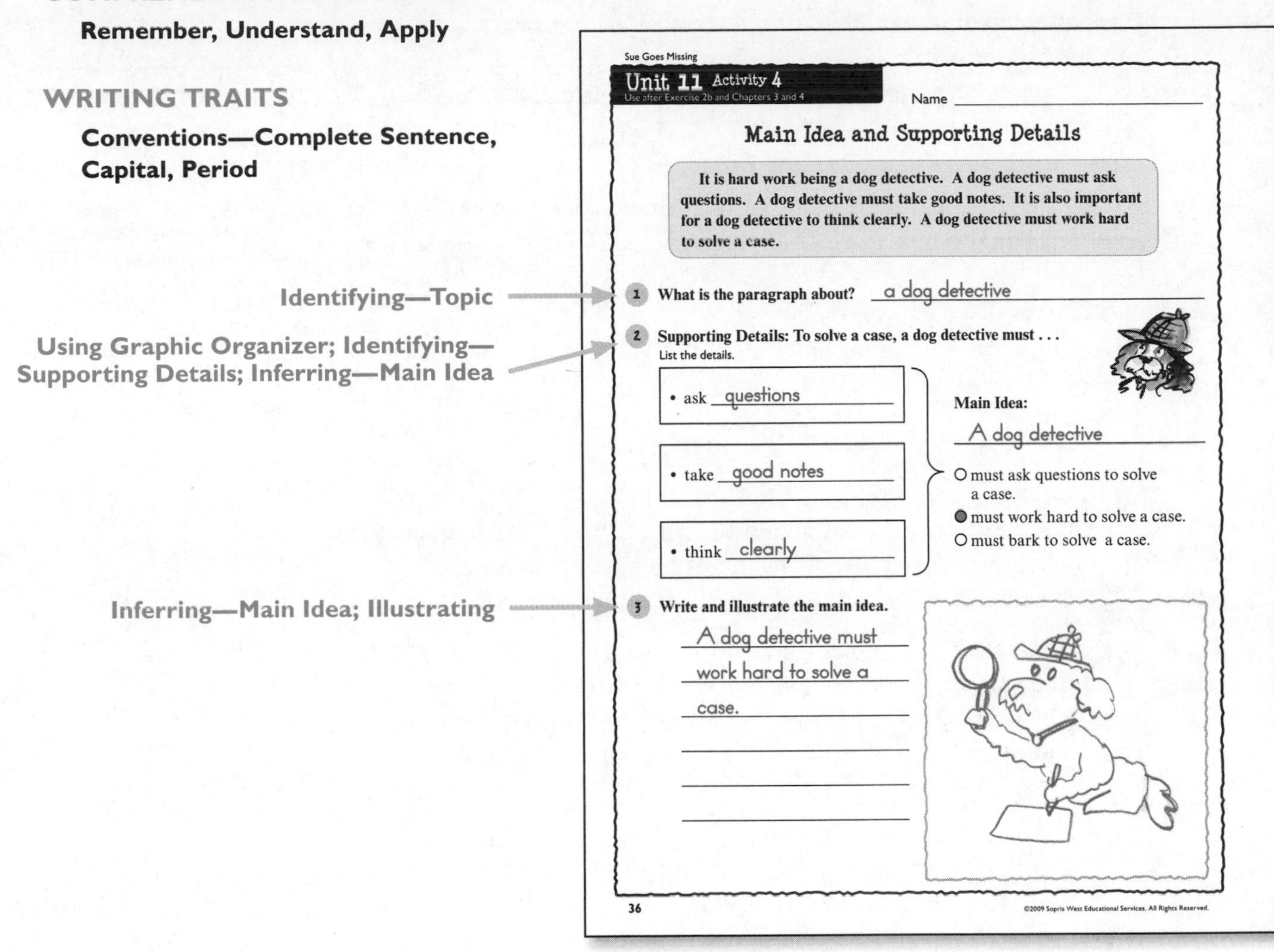

Sue Goes Missing

Unit 11 Activity 4
Use after Exercise 2b and Chapters 3 and 4

Name ____________

Main Idea and Supporting Details

It is hard work being a dog detective. A dog detective must ask questions. A dog detective must take good notes. It is also important for a dog detective to think clearly. A dog detective must work hard to solve a case.

1. What is the paragraph about? a dog detective

2. Supporting Details: To solve a case, a dog detective must . . .
List the details.

- ask questions
- take good notes
- think clearly

Main Idea: A dog detective
- ○ must ask questions to solve a case.
- ● must work hard to solve a case.
- ○ must bark to solve a case.

3. Write and illustrate the main idea.

A dog detective must work hard to solve a case.

36

©2009 Sopris West Educational Services. All Rights Reserved.

PROCEDURES

For each step, demonstrate and guide practice, as needed. Then have students complete the page independently.

1. **Topic: Answering Questions—Basic Instructions** (Item 1)
   - Have students read the paragraph.
   - Have students read the question and write the topic in the blank.

2. **Main Idea/Supporting Details: Hierarchy Chart—Basic Instructions** (Item 2)
   - Have students fill in the blanks to complete the supporting details.
   - Have students fill in the blank and a bubble to complete the main idea.

3. **Main Idea: Sentence Writing, Illustrating—Basic Instructions** (Item 3)
   Have students write the main idea sentence. Remind them to use a capital and a period. Then have students visualize and illustrate the main idea.

❶ SOUND REVIEW

PACING
Exercise 3a should take about 10 minutes, allowing about 10 minutes for the Descriptive Paragraph Focus Lesson.

★❷ NEW SOUND INTRODUCTION

- Have students look at the picture. Tell students e-a says /ĕĕĕ/ as in bread. Say something like:

  Look at the picture. Say "e-a says /ĕĕĕ/ as in bread." (e-a says /ĕĕĕ/ as in bread)
  Read the sentence. (Pam always spreads jam on her bread instead of butter.)
  Which three words have the /ĕĕĕ/ sound? (spreads, bread, instead)

- For Row B, have students read the underlined sound, then the word.
- After reading the row, have students go back and read the whole words.

❸ SOUND PRACTICE

For each task, have students spell and say the focus sound in the gray bar. Next, have students read each underlined sound, the word, then the whole column. Repeat practice.

❹ ACCURACY AND FLUENCY BUILDING

C1. Multisyllabic Words

- For the list of words divided by syllables, have students read each syllable, then the whole word. Use the word in a sentence, as appropriate.
- For the list of whole words, build accuracy and then fluency.

estimated I didn't know the exact amount, so I . . . *estimated.*
detective A person who solves mysteries is a . . . *detective.*
kidnapped The dogs were taken, or . . . *kidnapped.*
scientific The scientist's methods of study were . . . *scientific.*

E1. Tricky Words

- For each Tricky Word, have students use the sounds and word parts they know to silently sound out the word. Use the word in a sentence to help with pronunciation.
- If the word is unfamiliar, tell students the word.

height
Look at the first word. The word is *height*. Read the word. (height)
I am as tall as Juan. We are about the same . . . *height.*
Read the word three times. (height, height, height)

straight
Look at the next word. This word is tricky, but you can figure it out! The g-h is silent.
Sound out the word silently. Thumbs up when you know the word.
Read the word. (straight) The path was not crooked. It was . . . *straight.*
Read the word two times. (straight, straight)

weight
You know the next word. Read it. (weight) The nurse checked my height and . . . *weight.*
Read the word three times. (weight, weight, weight)

lazy The sloth slept all day. He was . . . *lazy.*

- Have students go back and read the whole words in the column.

★ = New in this unit

5 GENERALIZATION: READING NEW WORDS IN PARAGRAPHS

- Have students read the paragraph silently, then out loud. Tell students to use the sounds and word parts they know to read any difficult words.
- Repeat practice, as needed.

Sue Goes Missing

Unit 11 Exercise 3a
Use before Chapters 5 and 6

1. SOUND REVIEW Use selected Sound Cards from Units 1–11.

★2. NEW SOUND INTRODUCTION Introduce the new sound /ĕĕĕ/ as in bread.

A		
ea	bread	Pam always spreads jam on her bread instead of butter.

B head dead read thread heavy

3. SOUND PRACTICE In each column, have students spell and say the sound, then say any underlined sound and the word. Next, have students read the whole column.

oi	ai	i as in silent	Bossy E	Mixed Practice
soil	tail	silent	lake	quart
coin	brain	dino	sore	scent
point	waiting	dinosaur	quite	stew

4. ACCURACY AND FLUENCY BUILDING For each column, have students say any underlined part, then read each word. Next, have students read the whole column.

A1 Mixed Practice	B1 Reading by Analogy	C1 Multisyllabic Words	D1 Word Endings	E1 Tricky Words
crisp	sure	es•ti•mat•ed	camped	height
shot	treasure	de•tec•tive	lifted	straight
milk	measure	kid•napped	perking	weight
length	front	sci•en•tif•ic	following	lazy
A2 Compound Words	sons	estimated	pounds	
nickname	tons	detective	eats	
whatever		kidnapped	skulls	
notepad		scientific		

5. GENERALIZATION Have students read the paragraph silently, then out loud. (New words: Tish, August, worth)

Tish has a birthday in August. Mom and I searched and searched for the perfect present. I was getting distressed. I could not find a present. Finally we found a beautiful ring. It glistened in the sun. The hours of searching were worth it. We had found the perfect present!

28

LEARNING FROM MISTAKES (Reminder)

Mistakes are an important part of learning!

- If you hear a mistake, say something like: Oops, that was hard, but we can get it!
- Demonstrate or guide students on the correct skill or strategy (sound, sounding out, reading a word by parts . . .).
- Have the group practice the skill.
- Make sure the individual who made the mistake has an opportunity to demonstrate that he or she worked hard and got it.
- Give descriptive feedback. [Beth], you worked hard and now you can read the Tricky Word *straight*.

GENERALIZATION (Reminder)

The generalization task provides an opportunity for you to informally assess students' ability to read new words that have not been pretaught.

DESCRIPTIVE PARAGRAPH

FOCUS LESSON
Skills and Strategies

PURPOSE

The purpose of this lesson is to provide explicit instruction in how to use notes to write a descriptive paragraph. The lesson prepares students for Comprehension and Skill Work. Students do not write in their books.

PREP NOTES

To demonstrate how to write a descriptive paragraph, use an overhead of page 29 in student *Exercise Book 2*, write on a transparency placed over the page, or use a paper copy.

COMPREHENSION PROCESSES

Remember, Understand, Create

PACING

Exercise 3b should take about 10 minutes.

PROCEDURES

1 INTRODUCTION

- Read the first paragraph on page 70 of the storybook to students. After reading, say something like:

  Look at your Focus Lesson. We're going to use the copy of Sir Winston's notes to write a description of Sue.

- Explain the purpose of the lesson. Say something like:

  Writing a descriptive paragraph is a great strategy for remembering and understanding what you've read. We're going to use Sir Winston's notes to write a paragraph, then we'll read the rest of the chapter.

2 WRITING A DESCRIPTIVE PARAGRAPH

Identifying—Topic, What; Generating Ideas

- Introduce topic sentences. Say something like:

  The first sentence of a descriptive paragraph is a topic sentence—just like a fact summary.
  A topic sentence tells what the paragraph is going to be about.
  Everyone, read the beginning of the topic sentence. (The missing dinosaur, Sue, is a . . .)
  What's the most important information in Sir Winston's notes? (She is a T. rex.)
  I think I'll write it out. Read with me. A good topic sentence would be: The missing dinosaur is a Tyrannosaurus rex. **After "The missing dinosaur, Sue, is a," write "Tyrannosaurus rex."**

- Demonstrate and guide writing the first part of the description.

  Now we need to write details about the topic. Look at Sir Winston's notes.
  What else did he learn about Sue? (She was 67 million years old.)
  We could write, "Sue is 67 million years old."
  We could also write a more interesting sentence by adding more details or using snazzier words.
  We could write "Sue is *ancient*. She is 67 million years old."
  Write "Sue is ancient. She is 67 million years old!"

- Have students brainstorm what to write for the second part of the description.

  Partner 1, tell your partner a snazzy sentence using another detail or two.

  After about minute, have Partner 2 generate a description. Then say:

  What are some sentences you came up with? (People found Sue in North America in 1990. Sue is a whopping 42 feet long and weighs 7 tons . . .)
  Write something like "She is an enormous creature. She weighs about 7 tons."

- Have students read the paragraph and evaluate whether they would know what to look for after reading the description.

Dog Detective

Unit 11 Exercise 3b (Focus Lesson)
Use after Exercise 3a and before Chapter 5

FOCUS LESSON
Skills and Strategies

Descriptive Paragraph

Kidnapped

CLUES	
Scientific name:	*Tyrannosaurus rex*
Nickname:	Sue
Age:	67 million years old
Home:	North America
Found:	August 12, 1990
Length:	42 feet long
Height at hips:	13 feet
Estimated weight:	7 tons
Weight of skull:	600 pounds
Length of skull:	5 feet
Size of brain:	Just big enough to hold a quart of milk
Size of teeth:	5 to 12 inches long

Look at Sir Winston's clues. Write a short description of the missing dinosaur. Use at least two details.

(Topic) The missing dinosaur, Sue, is a Tyrannosaurus rex.

(Detail 1) Sue is ancient. She is 67 million years old.

(Detail 2) She is an enormous creature. She weighs 7 tons.

STOP Don't write in your Exercise Book.

CHAPTER 5 INSTRUCTIONS

Students read Chapter 5 with the teacher and Chapter 6 on their own.

COMPREHENSION PROCESSES

Remember, Understand, Apply, Create

PROCEDURES

1. Reviewing Chapter 4

Identifying—What; Inferring; Explaining; Predicting

Review what happened in Chapter 4 by quickly discussing the questions from Chapter 4, Setting a Purpose. Say something like:

Yesterday, you read Chapter 4 on your own. Let's see what you found out.

Who or what is missing? (A dinosaur, a T. rex, named Sue is missing.)

Why did Sir Winston get nervous?
(It's a very big case. He isn't sure he can solve the case.)

What does Sir Winston decide he can do? (He can solve the case.)

Do you think Sir Winston will solve the case? Why or why not?
(I think he will solve the case because he thinks he can. I think he will solve the case because he is the main character. I think he will solve the case because he is smart . . .)

2. Introducing Chapter 5

Identifying—Title, Explaining

Say something like:

We've already read the first paragraph.

What is the title of the chapter? (Kidnapped)

What does *kidnapped* mean? (Someone took Sue . . .)

What do you think has happened to Sue? (Maybe someone took her. Maybe she got lost.)

3. First Reading

- Ask questions and discuss the story as indicated by the gray text.
- Mix group and individual turns, independent of your voice. Have students work toward a group accuracy goal of 0–3 errors. Quietly keep track of errors made by all students in the group.
- After reading the story, practice any difficult words and reread, if appropriate.

4. Second Reading, Short Passage Practice: Developing Prosody

- Demonstrate expressive, fluent reading of the first two paragraphs.
- Guide practice with your voice.
- Provide individual turns while others track with their fingers and whisper read.
- Repeat with one paragraph or page at a time.

CORRECTING DECODING ERRORS

During story reading, gently correct any error, then have students reread the sentence.

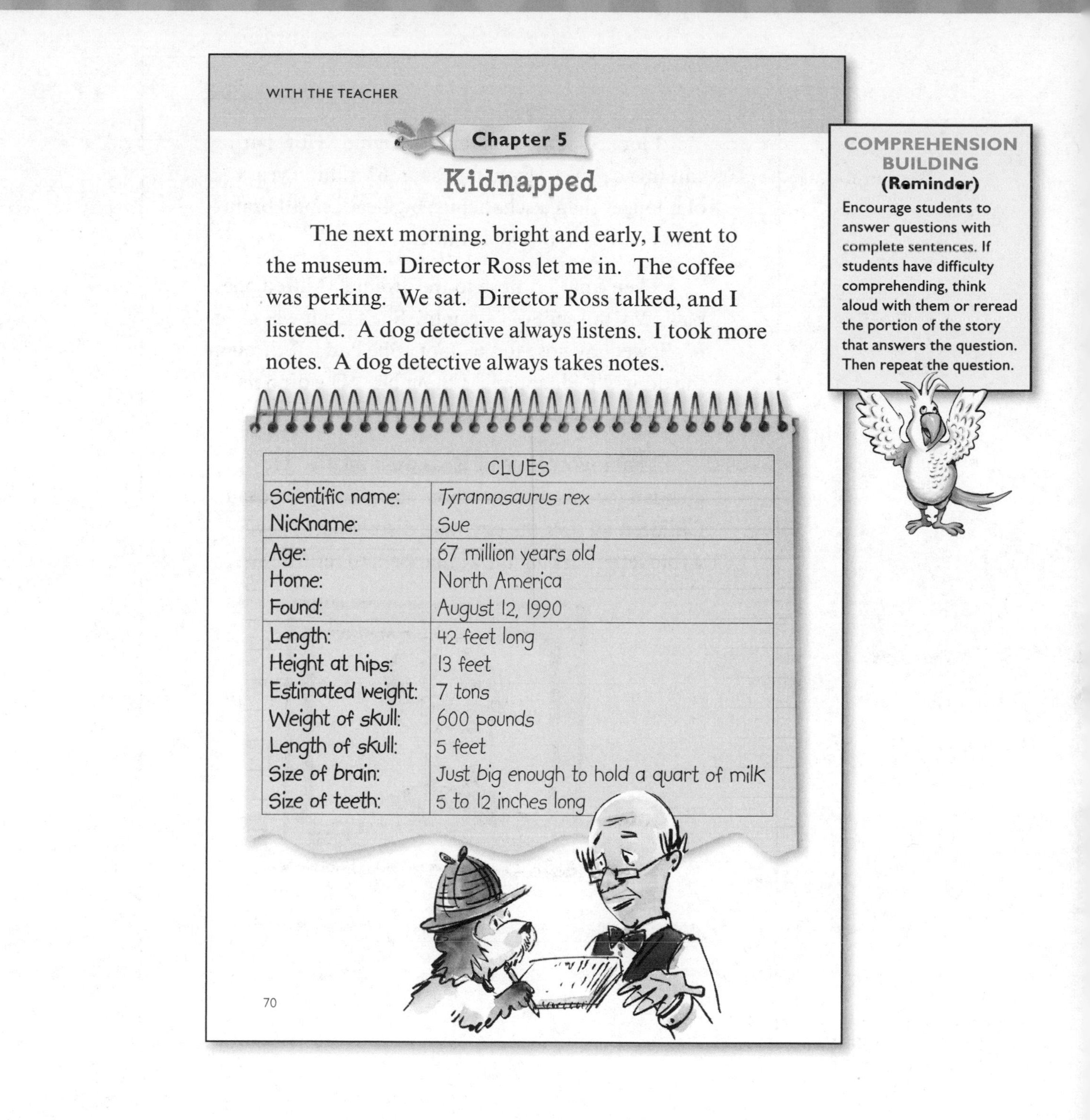

WITH THE TEACHER

Chapter 5

Kidnapped

The next morning, bright and early, I went to the museum. Director Ross let me in. The coffee was perking. We sat. Director Ross talked, and I listened. A dog detective always listens. I took more notes. A dog detective always takes notes.

CLUES	
Scientific name:	*Tyrannosaurus rex*
Nickname:	Sue
Age:	67 million years old
Home:	North America
Found:	August 12, 1990
Length:	42 feet long
Height at hips:	13 feet
Estimated weight:	7 tons
Weight of skull:	600 pounds
Length of skull:	5 feet
Size of brain:	Just big enough to hold a quart of milk
Size of teeth:	5 to 12 inches long

70

COMPREHENSION BUILDING
(Reminder)
Encourage students to answer questions with complete sentences. If students have difficulty comprehending, think aloud with them or reread the portion of the story that answers the question. Then repeat the question.

I looked at my clues and thought, "How hard can this be? Very large dinosaur, 67 million years old, longer than a school bus, big head, small brain—not very smart, probably hungry!"

Then I put my nose to the ground. I lifted one paw. My tail shot out straight. Sue's scent was clear. I followed my nose to the door. She had left through the door. "Kidnapped!" I thought. "The dino must have been kidnapped!"

That night Director Ross went on TV. He pleaded for information about the missing dinosaur. Children all over the city were distressed. They wrote letters asking the kidnappers to return Sue.

What does this dog detective do to solve a case?[1] What has Sir Winston learned about Sue?[2]

COMPREHENDING AS YOU GO

1. **Remember:** Identifying—What; **Understand:** Describing (He listens, takes notes, follows the scent.)
2. **Remember:** Locating Information; **Understand:** Describing (She is a Tyrannosaurus rex. She is 67 million years old. She was found August 12, 1990, in North America . . .)

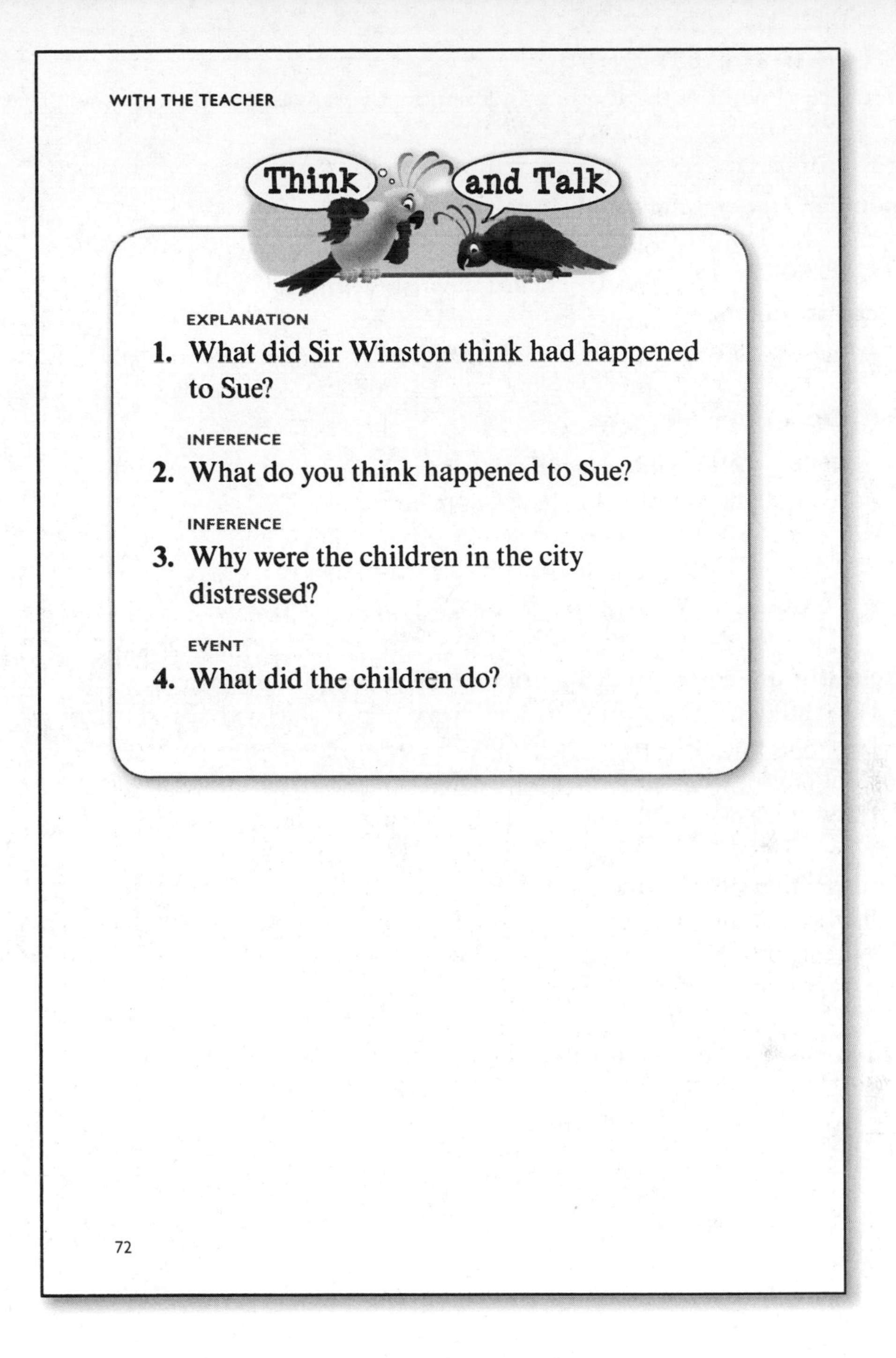

WITH THE TEACHER

Think and Talk

EXPLANATION

1. What did Sir Winston think had happened to Sue?

INFERENCE

2. What do you think happened to Sue?

INFERENCE

3. Why were the children in the city distressed?

EVENT

4. What did the children do?

72

1. **Understand:** Explaining (He thought Sue had been kidnapped.)
2. **Create:** Generating Ideas; **Apply:** Inferring (I think she has been kidnapped. I think she is lost. I think she is hiding . . .)
3. **Apply:** Inferring, Explaining; **Understand:** Using Vocabulary—distressed (They were distressed because they liked visiting the dinosaur at the museum. They missed Sue.)
4. **Understand:** Explaining—Event (They wrote letters asking the kidnappers to return Sue.)

CHAPTER 6 INSTRUCTIONS

Students read without the teacher, independently or with partners.

> **PREP NOTE**
> **Setting a Purpose**
> Write questions on a chalkboard, white board, or large piece of paper before working with your small group.

COMPREHENSION PROCESSES

Remember, Understand, Apply, Analyze

PROCEDURES

1. Getting Ready

Have students turn to Chapter 6 on page 73.

2. Setting a Purpose

Identifying—What; Inferring; Explaining

Before students begin reading, say something like:

Read to find out the answers to these questions:

- What did Sir Winston find?
- Why does Sir Winston say, "Well, I'll be. I wonder why"?

3. Reading on Your Own: Partner or Whisper Reading

- Have students take turns reading every other page with a partner or have students whisper read pages 73–75 on their own.
- Continue having students track each word with their fingers.
- Have students ask themselves or their partners the gray text questions.

4. Comprehension and Skill Work

Tell students they will do Comprehension and Skill Activities 5 and 6 after they read on their own. Guide practice, as needed. (For teacher directions, see pages 58 and 59.)

5. Homework 4: Repeated Reading

ON YOUR OWN

Chapter 6

Footprints

While the children wrote letters, the police searched through the city. I, dog detective, went back to the museum. I began by following my nose. Sue's scent went right through the door. I followed my nose. She had gone through the city and into the forest.

By eight, it was dark and my nose was quite sore. That T. rex had traveled a long, long way. I built a fire and opened a can of Lazy Dog Stew. I read my notes, and I thought. A dog detective always thinks.

The next morning, I got up at dawn. The air was cool, crisp, and clean. I stretched. I had camped near a lake. In the morning light, the blue water glistened. It almost felt like I was on a vacation. Then I saw the prints—huge dino prints in the mud.

It was then that I knew. I, Sir Winston, dog detective, would find the missing Sue.

How did Sir Winston end up near the lake?[1] How did Sir Winston know he would find Sue?[2]

73

COMPREHENDING AS YOU GO

1 **Understand:** Explaining (He followed Sue's scent to the lake.)

2 **Understand:** Explaining (He saw dinosaur footprints in the mud by the lake.)

ON YOUR OWN
DOG PACK
74

I cooked a good breakfast. A dog detective always eats breakfast. Then I packed up my things and carefully put out the fire.

Before leaving the lake, I measured the prints and wrote in my notepad "large dino prints near lake." I was ready to leave, but I thought, "I'm missing something. There's another clue here. What is it?" Then I knew! The only footprints by the lake belonged to the dino. I said to myself, "Well, I'll be. I wonder why."

Why do you think Sir Winston said, "Well, I'll be"?[1] What did Sir Winston figure out?[2] What do you think Sir Winston wondered?[3]

COMPREHENDING AS YOU GO

1. **Apply:** Inferring (Sir Winston was surprised . . .)
2. **Analyze:** Drawing Conclusions (Sir Winston figured out that Sue was by herself and that she had not been kidnapped.)
3. **Analyze:** Drawing Conclusions (He wondered why she left the museum on her own.)

STORY COMPREHENSION

COMPREHENSION PROCESSES

Remember, Understand, Create

WRITING TRAITS

Organization—Topic Sentence,
Supporting Details
Word Choice
Conventions—Period

Generating Ideas, Describing

Using Graphic Organizer
Explaining—Events

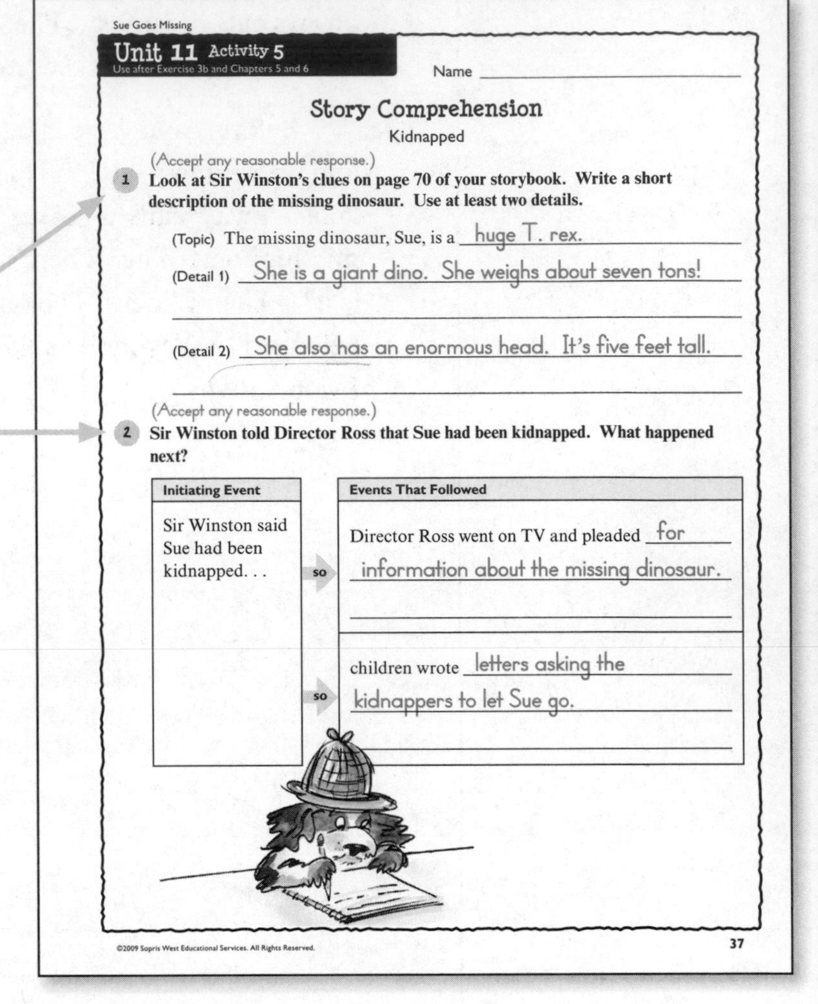

Sue Goes Missing

Unit 11 Activity 5
Use after Exercise 3b and Chapters 5 and 6

Name ________________

Story Comprehension

Kidnapped

(Accept any reasonable response.)

1 **Look at Sir Winston's clues on page 70 of your storybook. Write a short description of the missing dinosaur. Use at least two details.**

(Topic) The missing dinosaur, Sue, is a huge T. rex.

(Detail 1) She is a giant dino. She weighs about seven tons!

(Detail 2) She also has an enormous head. It's five feet tall.

(Accept any reasonable response.)

2 **Sir Winston told Director Ross that Sue had been kidnapped. What happened next?**

Initiating Event		Events That Followed
Sir Winston said Sue had been kidnapped. . .	so	Director Ross went on TV and pleaded for information about the missing dinosaur.
	so	children wrote letters asking the kidnappers to let Sue go.

37

PROCEDURES

Demonstrate and guide practice, as needed.

★ **1. Description: Paragraph Writing—Specific Instructions** (Item 1)

- Tell students they will write a descriptive paragraph like the one they did in the Focus Lesson. (See Exercise 3b.)
- Have students read the directions, then write a short descriptive paragraph.
- Guide students through the activity, only as needed.
- Remind students to check and correct their work.

★ **2. Cause/Effect: Sequence Chart—Specific Instructions** (Item 2)

- Have students read the directions. Then have students read the initiating event.

  Read the directions for Item 1. (Sir Winston told Director Ross that Sue had been kidnapped . . .)

  Read the initiating event. (Sir Winston said Sue had been kidnapped.)

  Touch the arrow and read the word in it. (so)

  The arrow shows that something happened next. Something happened *because* Sir Winston said that Sue had been kidnapped. Go to the next box. Read and tell what happened. (Director Ross went on TV and pleaded . . . for information about the missing dinosaur.)

  Now read the initiating event, the word "so," and your answer. (Sir Winston said Sue had been kidnapped, so Director Ross went on TV and pleaded for information about the missing dinosaur.)

  The chart shows how one thing led to the next. It shows the chain of events.

- Repeat with the second event, as needed.

★ = New in this unit

VOCABULARY AND SYNONYMS

COMPREHENSION PROCESSES

Understand, Apply

WRITING TRAITS

Conventions—Period

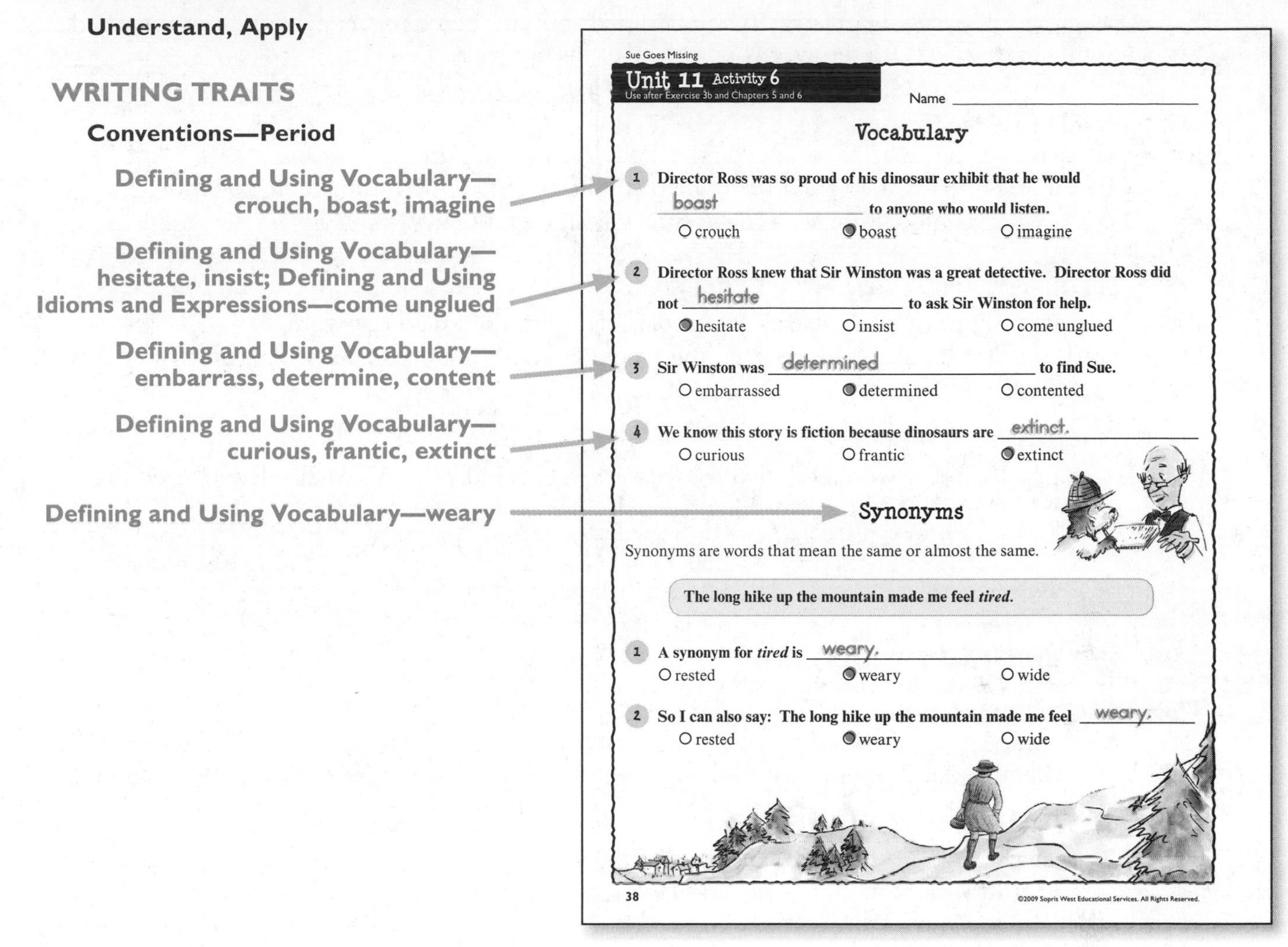

Sue Goes Missing

Unit 11 Activity 6
Use after Exercise 3b and Chapters 5 and 6

Name ________

Vocabulary

1. Director Ross was so proud of his dinosaur exhibit that he would boast to anyone who would listen.
   - O crouch ● boast O imagine
2. Director Ross knew that Sir Winston was a great detective. Director Ross did not hesitate to ask Sir Winston for help.
   - ● hesitate O insist O come unglued
3. Sir Winston was determined to find Sue.
   - O embarrassed ● determined O contented
4. We know this story is fiction because dinosaurs are extinct.
   - O curious O frantic ● extinct

Synonyms

Synonyms are words that mean the same or almost the same.

The long hike up the mountain made me feel *tired*.

1. A synonym for *tired* is weary.
   - O rested ● weary O wide
2. So I can also say: The long hike up the mountain made me feel weary.
   - O rested ● weary O wide

38

©2009 Sopris West Educational Services. All Rights Reserved.

PROCEDURES

For each step, demonstrate and guide practice, as needed. Then have students complete the page independently.

Vocabulary: Selection Response—Basic Instructions (Items 1–4)
Have students read each sentence, then fill in the bubble and blank with the correct vocabulary word. Remind students to put a period at the end of sentences.

Synonyms: Selection Response—Basic Instructions (Items 1, 2)
Have students read the sentence in the box, then fill in the bubble and blank with the vocabulary word that correctly completes the sentences. Remind students to put a period at the end of sentences.

Self-monitoring
Have students read their sentences to see if they make sense.

1 SOUND REVIEW

2 SHIFTY WORD BLENDING

For each word, have students say the underlined sound. Then have them sound out the word smoothly and say it. Use the words in sentences, as appropriate.

3 SOUND PRACTICE

- For each task, have students spell and say the focus sound in the gray bar.
  Next, have students read each underlined sound, the word, then the whole column.
- Repeat with each column, building accuracy first, then fluency.

4 ACCURACY AND FLUENCY BUILDING

- For each task, have students say any underlined part, then read the word.
- Set a pace. Then have students read the whole words in each task and column.
- Provide repeated practice, building accuracy first, then fluency.

C1. Multisyllabic Words

- For the list of words divided by syllables, have students read each syllable, then the whole word. Use the word in a sentence, as appropriate.
- For the list of whole words, build accuracy and then fluency.

afterword A part of a book that tells what happened after the story is an . . . *afterword.*
matter It wasn't important. It didn't . . . *matter.*
promised Dad said he'd buy me a horse. He . . . *promised.*

E1. Tricky Words

- For each Tricky Word, have students use the sounds and word parts they know to silently sound out the word. Use the word in a sentence to help with pronunciation.

touched The feather tickled my nose when it . . . *touched* . . . me.
gives Every year for my birthday, Mom . . . *gives* . . . me a present.
mountains There was lots of snow on top of the . . . *mountains.*
wonder How did dinosaurs die out? Do you ever . . . *wonder?*
worry Don't be upset. Don't . . . *worry.*
worried When Amanda's pet rabbit ran away, she . . . *worried.*

- Have students go back and read the whole words in the column.

5 OPEN SYLLABLE I

- Tell students the i in each of these words says its name.
- Have students read any underlined part, then the word.

6 GENERALIZATION: READING NEW WORDS IN PARAGRAPHS

- Have students read the paragraph silently, then out loud. Tell students to use the sounds and word parts they know to read any difficult words.
- Repeat practice, as needed.

Sue Goes Missing

Unit 11 Exercise 4

Use before Chapter 7

1. SOUND REVIEW Use selected Sound Cards from Units 1–11.

2. SHIFTY WORD BLENDING For each word, have students say the underlined part, sound out smoothly, then read the word.

own	known	flown	clown	clean

3. SOUND PRACTICE In each column, have students spell and say the sound, then say any underlined sound and the word. Next, have students read the whole column.

oi	ea as in bread	oa	ce	Mixed Practice
voice toilet oil	already weather ahead	roamed roared loaded	since office distance	town blue agreed

4. ACCURACY AND FLUENCY BUILDING For each column, have students say any underlined part, then read each word. Next, have students read the whole column.

A1 Word Endings	B1 Morphographs & Affixes	C1 Multisyllabic Words	D1 Related Words	E1 Tricky Words
strolled tracking barked begging spotted twinkled	exploring biweekly description colorful neatly return	af•ter•word mat•ter prom•ised afterword matter promised	bore bored boring celebrate celebrated celebrations	touched gives mountains wonder worry worried

5. OPEN SYLLABLE I Have students practice reading /ī/ and the related words.

i	pi•lot	i•dea	Chi•na	di•no	i•tem

6. GENERALIZATION Have students read the paragraph silently, then out loud. (New words: spice, flattered, exhibit)

Today was the grand opening of the new museum of natural history. The museum was loaded with flowers and balloons. People brought food and drinks to celebrate the special day. The museum director baked a cake for the first time. The spice cake was surprisingly good. The director was flattered when everyone said the cake was delicious. There was even an exhibit of dinosaurs and their young. I couldn't wait to see it!

30

BUILDING INDEPENDENCE (Reminder)

Some students will try to follow your voice instead of learning to read the sounds and words. Therefore, it is important for you to demonstrate and guide practice only as needed.

Give students many opportunities to respond without your assistance—with groups and individuals. Encourage independence.

CHAPTER 7 INSTRUCTIONS

Students read Chapter 7 with the teacher.

COMPREHENSION PROCESSES

Remember, Understand, Apply, Evaluate

PROCEDURES

1. Reviewing Chapter 6

Explaining; Identifying—What; Inferring; Explaining

- Review what happened in Chapter 6. Say something like:
  What did Sir Winston do to find Sue? (He followed his nose. He found dinosaur tracks.)
- Quickly discuss the questions from Setting a Purpose. Say something like:
  Yesterday, you read Chapter 6 on your own. Let's see what you found out.
  What did Sir Winston find? (He found large dino prints near the lake.)
  Why does Sir Winston say, "Well, I'll be. I wonder why?"
  (The only footprints by the lake belonged to the dino.)
  Yes, that's right. We can read between the lines and figure out what that means.
  Did the kidnappers leave footprints? (no)
  So what do you know about Sue? (She wasn't kidnapped.)
  That's right. We are great detectives, just like Sir Winston.
  What do you think happened to Sue if she wasn't kidnapped?

2. Introducing Chapter 7

Identifying—Title; Explaining

Say something like: What's the title of the chapter? (Tracking Sue)
What does *tracking* mean? (It means following footprints.)

3. First Reading

- Ask questions and discuss the story as indicated by the gray text.
- Mix group and individual turns, independent of your voice.
  Have students work toward a group accuracy goal of 0–5 errors.
- After reading the story, practice any difficult words.
  Reread the story if students have not reached the accuracy goal.

4. Second Reading, Timed Readings: Repeated Reading

- As time allows, have students do Timed Readings while others follow along.
- Time individuals for 30 seconds and encourage each child to work for a personal best.

5. Partner or Whisper Reading: Repeated Reading

Before beginning independent work, have students finger track and partner or whisper read.

6. Comprehension and Skill Work

Tell students they will do Comprehension and Skill Activities 7 and 8 after they read Chapter 7. Guide practice, as needed. (For teacher directions, see pages 69 and 70.)

7. Homework 4: Repeated Reading

WITH THE TEACHER

Chapter 7

Tracking Sue

I followed Sue's trail through the forest and mountains, then through cities and small towns. A dog detective never gives up. I knew I would find her. It was just a matter of time.

Days later, in a small place named Cozy Town, I spotted her. She wasn't easy to miss. She was playing in the park with a dozen kids at her feet. A young girl sat on Sue's head. I watched from a distance. Sue's big teeth glistened in the sun.

Sue looked happy. Since that day at the lake, I'd known. The only tracks I'd found were Sue's. There weren't any kidnappers. Sue had left on her own.

Where did Sir Winston find Sue?[1] Who was she with?[2] How do you think Sue got to Cozy Town?[3]

76

COMPREHENDING AS YOU GO

❶ **Remember:** Identifying—Where (Sir Winston found Sue in Cozy Town.)

❷ **Remember:** Identifying—Who (Sue was with a bunch of kids.)

❸ **Apply:** Inferring (Sue walked to Cozy Town . . .)

SUE GOES MISSING
77

WITH THE TEACHER

I strolled over to Sue. She looked at me with surprisingly blue eyes. Then she roared, "How do you do? My name is Sue."

I grinned back. "Fine thanks," I barked. "My name is Sir Winston. Director Ross sent me. He's ever so worried. Where have you been?"

Sue giggled and said, "I've been on an adventure—I have! I was bored at the museum, so one night I just walked out the door. I roamed through forests, mountains, cities, and towns. Then I found a nice house and a new best friend." Sue's big blue eyes twinkled.

I saw that the dino was happy and not about to return to the museum. Now what to do? I scratched my head.

You may wonder how this all turned out. I called Director Ross and he came to Cozy Town. He came loaded with letters from kids all over the country begging for Sue's return. Sue was flattered. She was touched. She was happy to be loved.

Why did Sue leave the museum?[1] What made her feel flattered, happy, and loved?[2] What do you think will happen next?[3]

78

COMPREHENDING AS YOU GO

1. **Understand:** Explaining (Sue left the museum because she was bored.)
2. **Understand:** Explaining (The letters from kids all over the country made Sue feel happy and loved.)
3. **Apply:** Predicting (Sue will go back to the museum because all the kids love her. Sue will stay in Cozy Town because the museum is boring . . .)

Ross and Sue talked and talked. Finally, Sue agreed to go back to the museum, and Director Ross promised her time off. Sue would get two days off each week and two weeks off each year.

Ross, Sue, and I went back to the city. A big commotion followed—lights, cameras, celebrations! Case closed!

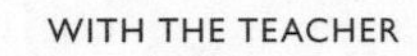

WITH THE TEACHER

Afterword: Now two days a week and two weeks each year, in the dark of night, Sue walks out the museum door. She returns to Cozy Town where she laughs, plays games, and goes exploring with her new best friend.

80

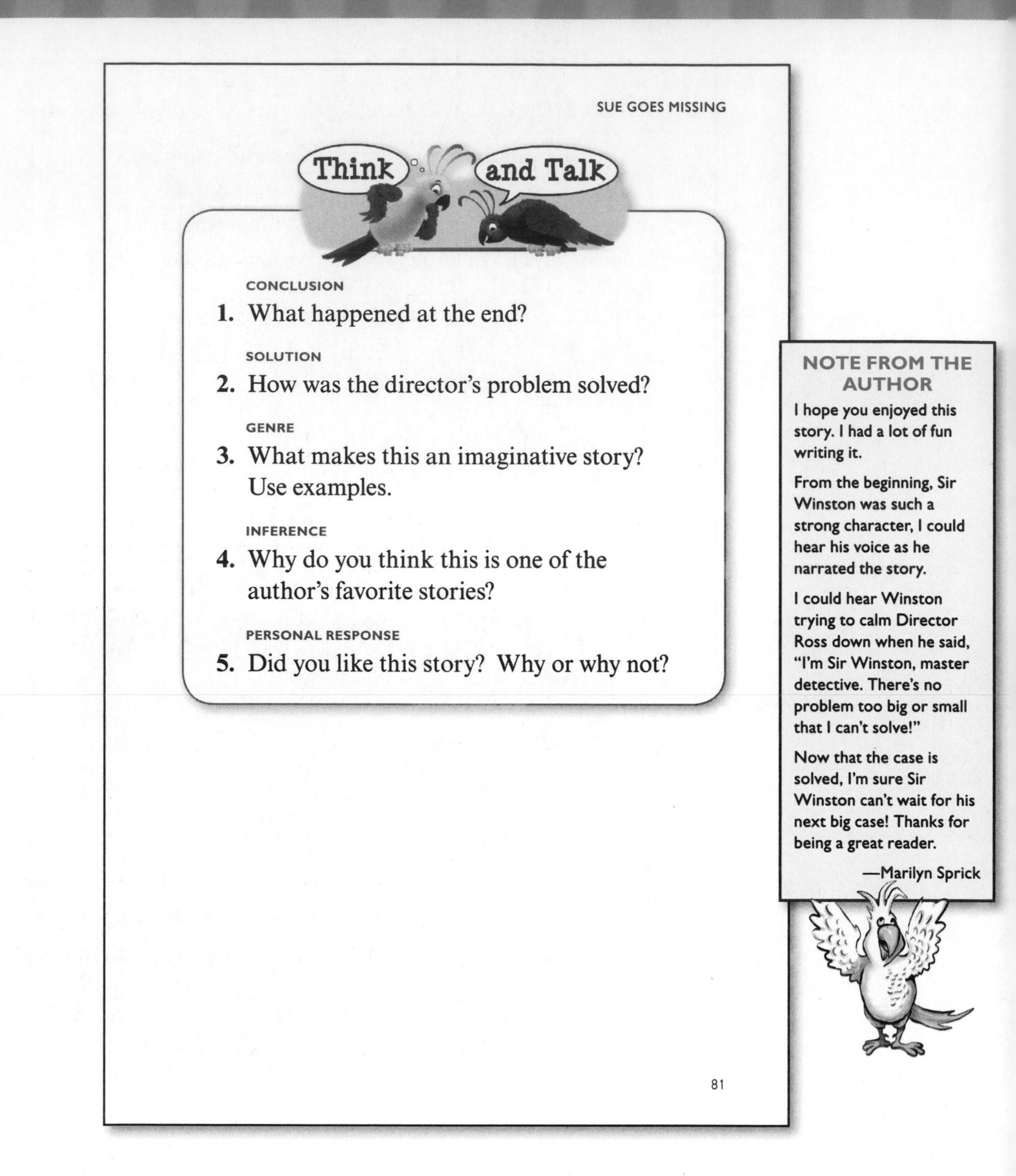

SUE GOES MISSING

CONCLUSION

1. What happened at the end?

SOLUTION

2. How was the director's problem solved?

GENRE

3. What makes this an imaginative story? Use examples.

INFERENCE

4. Why do you think this is one of the author's favorite stories?

PERSONAL RESPONSE

5. Did you like this story? Why or why not?

81

NOTE FROM THE AUTHOR

I hope you enjoyed this story. I had a lot of fun writing it.

From the beginning, Sir Winston was such a strong character, I could hear his voice as he narrated the story.

I could hear Winston trying to calm Director Ross down when he said, "I'm Sir Winston, master detective. There's no problem too big or small that I can't solve!"

Now that the case is solved, I'm sure Sir Winston can't wait for his next big case! Thanks for being a great reader.

—Marilyn Sprick

❶ **Understand:** Explaining—End/Conclusion (Sue and the director worked out a deal.)

❷ **Understand:** Explaining—Solution (Sue came back to the museum but got to take off two days a week and two weeks a year.)

❸ **Apply:** Explaining—Genre; Using Vocabulary—imagination (A dog is a detective, and a dinosaur walks out of a museum. These things can't really happen. The author had a great imagination . . .)

❹ **Apply:** Inferring (I think this is one of the author's favorite stories because Mrs. Sprick said she had lots of fun writing it.)

❺ **Evaluate:** Responding (I liked it because the characters were fun, and I didn't know what was going to happen.)

PASSAGE READING FLUENCY

FLUENCY

Accuracy, Expression, Rate

PROCEDURES

For each step, demonstrate and guide practice, as needed. Then have students complete the page independently.

Passage Reading—Basic Instructions

- Have students read the practice words.
- Have students finger track and whisper read the story two times—the first time for accuracy and the second time for expression. Have students cross out a dinosaur each time they finish.
- Have students do a one-minute Timed Reading and cross out the timer. Say something like:

You are going to track with your finger and whisper read.

Read the passage three times. The first time, read for accuracy.

What will you read for? (accuracy)

The second time, read for accuracy and expression. What will you read for? (accuracy and expression)

Each time you read, cross out a dinosaur, and notice how much better your reading sounds.

The last time you read, use the timer. Read quickly, but accurately and with expression.

See if you can finish reading before one minute is up.

Sue Goes Missing

Unit 11 Activity 7

Use after Exercise 4 and Chapter 7

Name ____________________

Passage Reading Fluency

1. Practice these words:

guard	expedition	daydream	imagination

2. Read the story 2 times. Cross out a dinosaur each time you read the story.

Dino Daydreams

Dan finishes his homework, then heads for the Hall of Dinosaurs. His father is the museum director. Dan gets to roam around the museum every day after school. 11 23 28

"Find any bones lately?" the guard asks. 35

"I wish," Dan says. He and his father had found a fossil for the museum the summer before. Locating fossils is their specialty. 49 58

Dan can't wait to go fossil hunting again this summer. He loves everything about the expeditions. In a moment, his imagination takes him there. He smells the campfire in the cool morning air. He sees the map on the computer showing where the bones should be. His heart pounds with excitement as they dig the first bone out of the mud. 70 80 94 106 119

"Daydreaming again?" the guard asks. 124

"Yup." Dan grins. He can't wait to find another fossil. Maybe this time it will be a T. rex. 136 143

3. Set a timer and see how far you can read in one minute. Then cross out the timer.

©2009 Sopris West Educational Services. All Rights Reserved.

39

ACCURACY PRECEDES RATE (Reminder)

Students should read the story with a high degree of accuracy before proceeding to Timed Readings. Reading for increased rate before establishing a high degree of accuracy may encourage students to guess at words.

STORY MAP

COMPREHENSION PROCESSES

Understand, Apply

WRITING TRAITS

Conventions—Capital, Period

PROCEDURES

Use an overhead BLM copy of the story map to demonstrate and guide practice, as needed.

Story Map: Character Web, Sentence Completion—Basic Instructions

- Have students complete each section of the story map: introduction, beginning, middle, and end. Remind students to put a period at the end of a sentence.
- For some groups, provide students with time to complete each section before you move to the next.
- For more independent writers, demonstrate and guide how to complete the entire story map, then have students complete their own map independently.

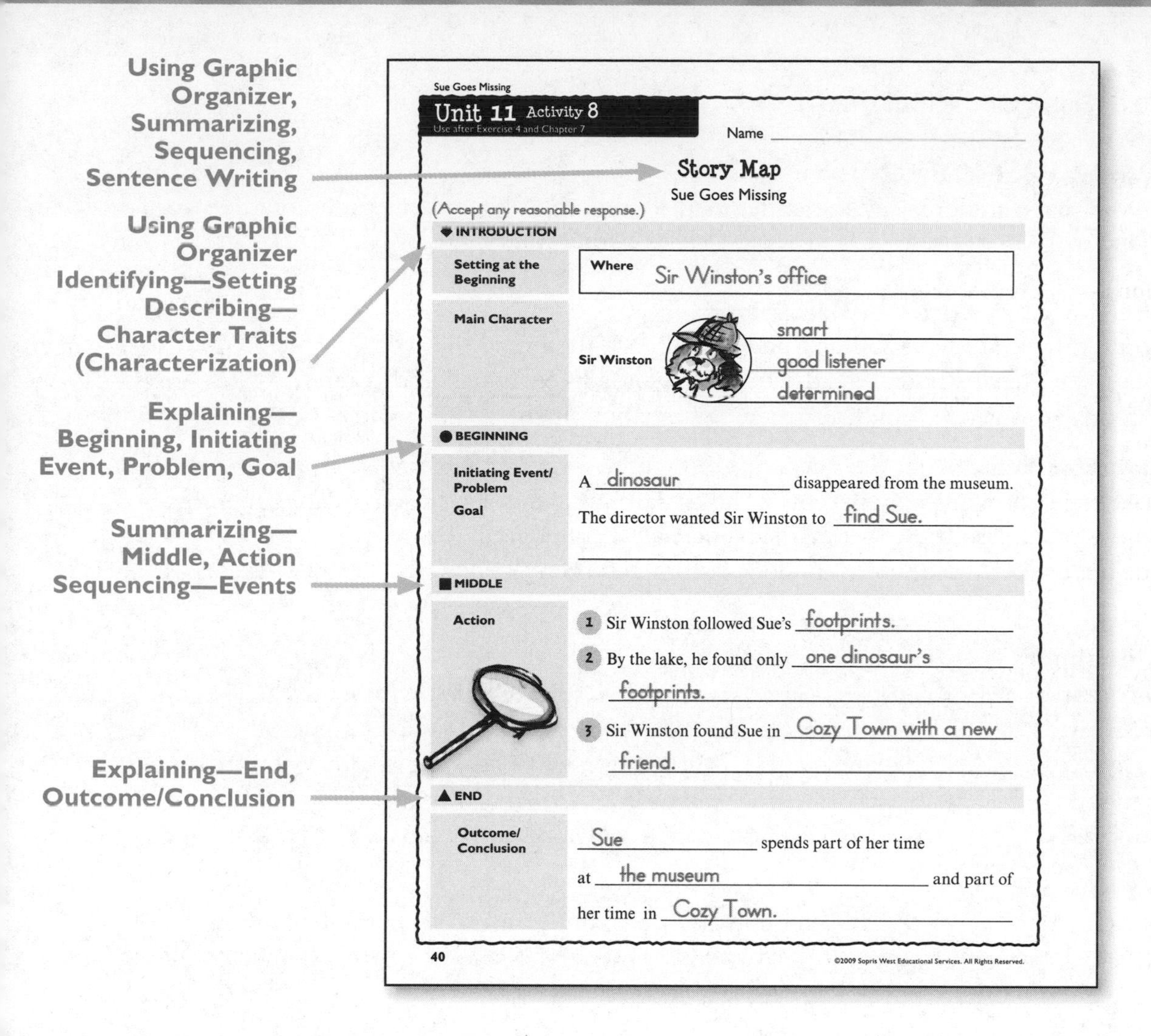

Sue Goes Missing

Unit 11 Activity 8
Use after Exercise 4 and Chapter 7

Name ____________

Story Map
Sue Goes Missing

(Accept any reasonable response.)

◆ INTRODUCTION

Setting at the Beginning — Where: Sir Winston's office

Main Character — Sir Winston: smart, good listener, determined

● BEGINNING

Initiating Event/Problem — A dinosaur disappeared from the museum.

Goal — The director wanted Sir Winston to find Sue.

■ MIDDLE

Action

1. Sir Winston followed Sue's footprints.
2. By the lake, he found only one dinosaur's footprints.
3. Sir Winston found Sue in Cozy Town with a new friend.

▲ END

Outcome/Conclusion — Sue spends part of her time at the museum and part of her time in Cozy Town.

40

❶ SOUND REVIEW

Use selected Sound Cards from Units 1–11.

❷ SHIFTY WORD BLENDING

For each word, have students say the underlined sound. Then have them sound out the word smoothly and say it. Use the words in sentences, as appropriate.

❸ ACCURACY AND FLUENCY BUILDING

- For each task, have students say any underlined part, then read the word.
- Set a pace. Then have students read the whole words in each task and column.
- Provide repeated practice, building accuracy first, then fluency.

C1. Multisyllabic Words

- For the list of words divided by syllables, have students read each syllable, then the whole word. Use the word in a sentence, as appropriate.
- For the list of whole words, build accuracy and then fluency.

simply	He did not go into details. He . . . *simply* . . . told the facts.
kidnappers	The police arrested the . . . *kidnappers.*
interest	Keeping Sue in bed while she was sick was in her best . . . *interest.*
exhibit	The class went to the museum to see the dinosaur . . . *exhibit.*
support	The community gave Sir Henry a lot of help and . . . *support.*
perhaps	Another way to say maybe is . . . *perhaps.*
succeeds	We hope Bill wins the race. We hope he . . . *succeeds.*

D1. Tricky Words

- For each Tricky Word, have students use the sounds and word parts they know to silently sound out the word. Use the word in a sentence to help with pronunciation.

sure	Jade knew the answer was correct. She was . . . *sure.*
greatest	He is so great. He is the . . . *greatest.*
answer	If someone asks you a question, you should . . . *answer.*
people	The room was crowded. There were a lot of . . . *people.*

- Have students go back and read the whole words in the column.

❹ WORD ENDINGS

Have students read the underlined word, then the word with an ending.

❺ MORPHOGRAPHS AND AFFIXES

- Have students read the underlined part, then the word.
- Repeat practice with whole words, mixing group and individual turns. Build accuracy, then fluency.

❻ GENERALIZATION: READING NEW WORDS IN PARAGRAPHS

- Have students read the paragraph silently, then out loud. Tell students to use the sounds and word parts they know to read any difficult words.
- Repeat practice, as needed.

Fluency

Unit 11 Exercise 5
Use before Dog Detective Succeeds

1. SOUND REVIEW Use selected Sound Cards from Units 1–11.

2. SHIFTY WORD BLENDING For each word, have students say the underlined part, sound out smoothly, then read the word.

left	ledge	leg	peg	page

3. ACCURACY AND FLUENCY BUILDING For each column, have students say any underlined part, then read each word. Next, have students read the whole column.

A1 Sound Practice	B1 Mixed Practice	C1 Multisyllabic Words		D1 Tricky Words
bread	quick	sim•ply	simply	sure
read	knew	kid•nap•pers	kidnappers	greatest
ready	per	in•ter•est	interest	answer
	Friday	ex•hi•bit	exhibit	people
roamed		sup•port	support	
throat		per•haps	perhaps	
loads		suc•ceeds	succeeds	

4. WORD ENDINGS Have students read the underlined word, then the word with an ending.

gotten	uses	closed	weeks

5. MORPHOGRAPHS AND AFFIXES Have students read the underlined word part, then the word.

A	unharmed	safely	remain	wonderful
B	unsolved	carefully	finally	comfortable

6. GENERALIZATION Have students read the paragraph silently, then out loud. (New words: December, difficult, mystery, truckloads)

It was December. Five long, difficult months had already passed. The detectives had been working hard to solve the mystery of the missing gems. Alexander said, "It appears that we will never solve this mystery! We have gone through truckloads of information. We have searched everywhere."

Sir Winston stated, "A good detective never gives up! We will succeed."

31

MASTERY TEACHING/ DISCRIMINATION PRACTICE

Repeated Practice

Provide repeated practice on each task. If you hear an error, gently correct the whole group with a demonstration and/or guided practice. Move to another skill or task, then return to the difficult item many times—mixing group and individual turns, independent of your voice. When a task is easy, build speed of recognition.

Remember, practice makes perfect! And practice builds fluency.

FLUENCY PASSAGE INSTRUCTIONS

This Story Reading targets fluency as the primary goal of instruction and practice. Students do Repeated Readings of this short passage to improve accuracy, expression, and rate.

COMPREHENSION PROCESSES

Remember, Understand, Analyze

PROCEDURES

1. Warm-Up: Partner or Whisper Reading

Before beginning group Story Reading, have students finger track and partner or whisper read the selection.

2. First Reading

- Ask questions as indicated by the gray text.
- Mix group and individual turns, independent of your voice. Have students work toward a group accuracy goal of 0–4 errors. Quietly keep track of errors made by all students in the group.
- After reading the story, practice any difficult words. Reread the story if students have not reached the accuracy goal.

3. Second Reading, Short Passage Practice: Developing Prosody

- Demonstrate reading the first paragraph with expression and fluency. Have students finger track as you read.
- Have students choral read the first paragraph. Encourage reading with expression and fluency.
- Repeat with second paragraph.

4. Third Reading, Group Timed Readings: Repeated Reading

- Encourage each child to work for a personal best. Have students whisper read for a one-minute Timed Reading. Tell students to go back to the top of the page and keep reading until the minute is up.
- Have students put their finger on the last word they read and count the number of words read correctly in one minute.
- Have students do a second Timed Reading of the same page.
- Have students try to beat their last score.
- Celebrate improvements.

5. Comprehension and Skill

Tell students they will do Comprehension and Skill Activities 9a and 9b after they read "Dog Detective Succeeds." Guide practice, as needed. (For teacher directions, see pages 79 and 81.)

6. Homework 5: Repeated Reading

CHECKOUT OPPORTUNITY

While students are Partner Reading, listen to individuals read the passage. Work on accuracy and fluency, as needed.

CORRECTING DECODING ERRORS

During story reading, gently correct any error, then have students reread the sentence.

WITH THE TEACHER

Fluency

WEATHER
High Humidity with rain showers expected.

Chicago Times FINAL

DOG DETECTIVE SUCCEEDS

from the *Chicago Times*
by reporter Bea Gull

After weeks on 3
the trail of the missing 8
dinosaur, Sir Winston, 11
master detective, and 14
Ross, museum director, 17
returned to the city with 22
Sue. The T. rex is now safely standing in 31
the Hall of Dinosaurs. She appears to 38
have been unharmed. 41

When asked about the mystery, Sir 47
Winston said, "It was a long and difficult 55
case, but I knew all along that I would 64
find Sue. A dog detective uses his nose. 72
There is no problem too big or small for a 82
dog detective!" 84

82

FINGER TRACKING (Reminder)

To maintain attention and build fluency, continue having students track text with their fingers. Provide positive feedback and individual turns to students who are finger tracking.

At the museum, Director Ross was quick 7
to say, "Sir Winston is a great detective, 15
perhaps the greatest detective of all time." 22

Director Ross also stated, "The 27
truckloads of letters from kids across the 34
country were important in getting Sue back. 41
Without the letters of support and everyone's 48
love, we may not have gotten Sue back." 56

WITH THE TEACHER

Fluency

The Hall of Dinosaurs is now back open— 8
five days per week, Saturday, Sunday, 14
Monday, Tuesday, and Wednesday. The 19
exhibit will be closed every Thursday and 26
Friday and the first week in August and 34
December. 35

When asked why the Hall would be 42
closed, Director Ross simply said, "It's in the 50
best interest of Sue and the museum. Our 58
other wonderful exhibits—the mummies, 63
gems, space, and so on—will remain open 71
seven days a week." 75

When asked where Sue had been and 82
what happened to the kidnappers, Director 88
Ross and Sir Winston had no answer. Some 96
people say that Sue was unhappy and left, 104
but we do not know for sure. 111

Who solved the case of the missing dinosaur? 1 Why is the dino exhibit closed two days each week and two weeks each year? 2 Why won't Sir Winston and Director Ross explain why Sue was missing? 3

84

COMPREHENDING AS YOU GO

1. **Remember:** Identifying—Who (Sir Winston solved the case of the missing dinosaur.)
2. **Understand:** Explaining (It is best for Sue and the museum. It is closed so Sue can go back to Cozy Town to visit her friends.)
3. **Analyze:** Drawing Conclusions (They don't want people to know that Sue was not happy at the museum . . .)

DOG DETECTIVE SUCCEEDS
85

WRITTEN RETELL

COMPREHENSION PROCESSES

Remember, Understand, Apply, Evaluate

WRITING TRAITS

Ideas and Content
Organization—Sequencing
Word Choice
Conventions—Complete Sentence, Capital, Period
Presentation

PROCEDURES

Use an overhead BLM copy of the story map to demonstrate and guide how to create a written retell.

Written Retell: Paragraph Writing—Basic Instructions

- Guide students, only as needed, as they construct an introductory paragraph using the information from their story map. You may wish to brainstorm phrases that describe the main character before they start.
- Repeat for the beginning and middle of the story, using the information from the story map. Remind students to start each sentence with a capital and end with a period.

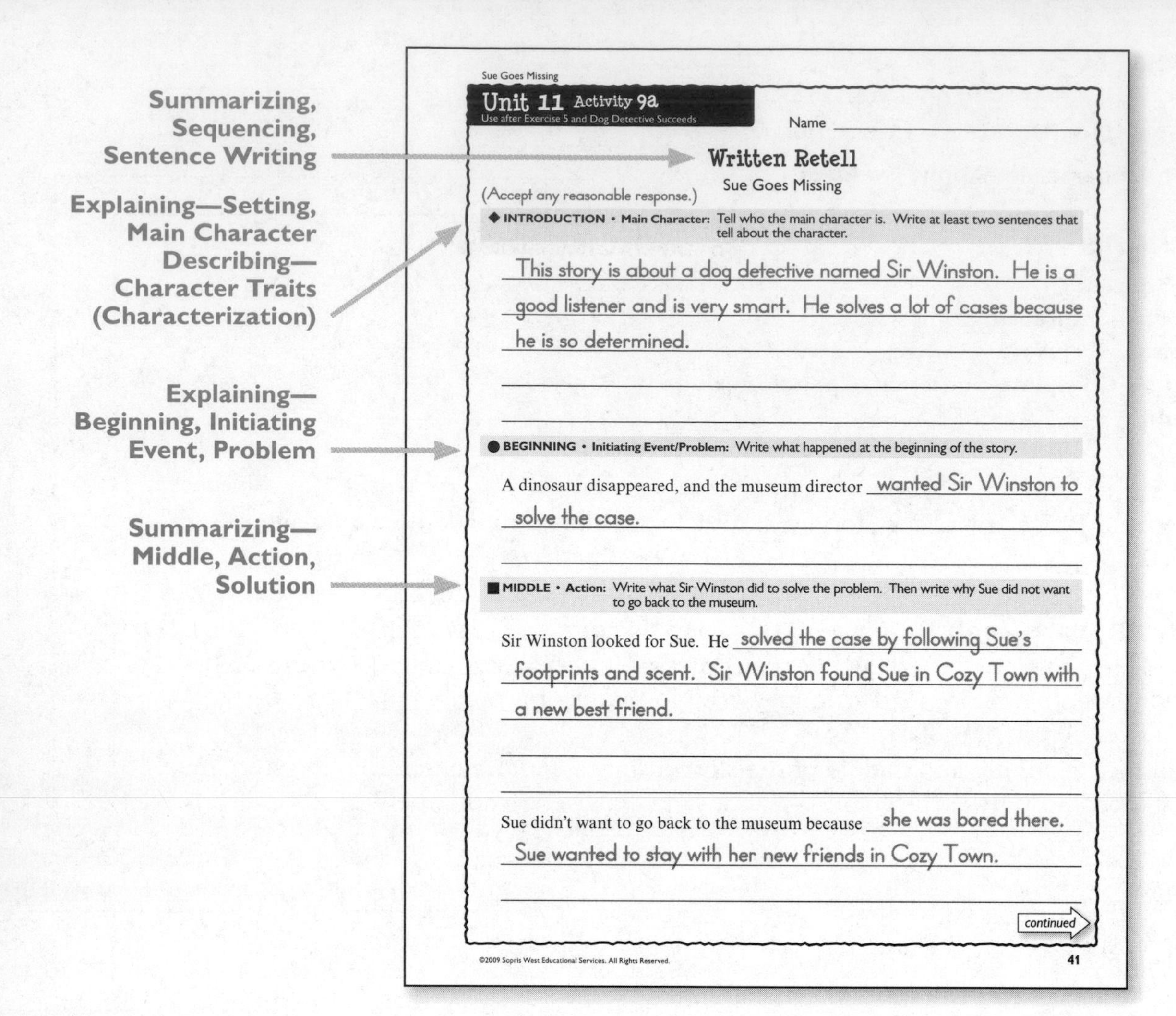

Sue Goes Missing

Unit 11 Activity 9a
Use after Exercise 5 and Dog Detective Succeeds

Name ______________________

Written Retell

Sue Goes Missing

(Accept any reasonable response.)

◆ **INTRODUCTION • Main Character:** Tell who the main character is. Write at least two sentences that tell about the character.

This story is about a dog detective named Sir Winston. He is a good listener and is very smart. He solves a lot of cases because he is so determined.

● **BEGINNING • Initiating Event/Problem:** Write what happened at the beginning of the story.

A dinosaur disappeared, and the museum director wanted Sir Winston to solve the case.

■ **MIDDLE • Action:** Write what Sir Winston did to solve the problem. Then write why Sue did not want to go back to the museum.

Sir Winston looked for Sue. He solved the case by following Sue's footprints and scent. Sir Winston found Sue in Cozy Town with a new best friend.

Sue didn't want to go back to the museum because she was bored there. Sue wanted to stay with her new friends in Cozy Town.

continued

41

WRITTEN RETELL *(continued)*

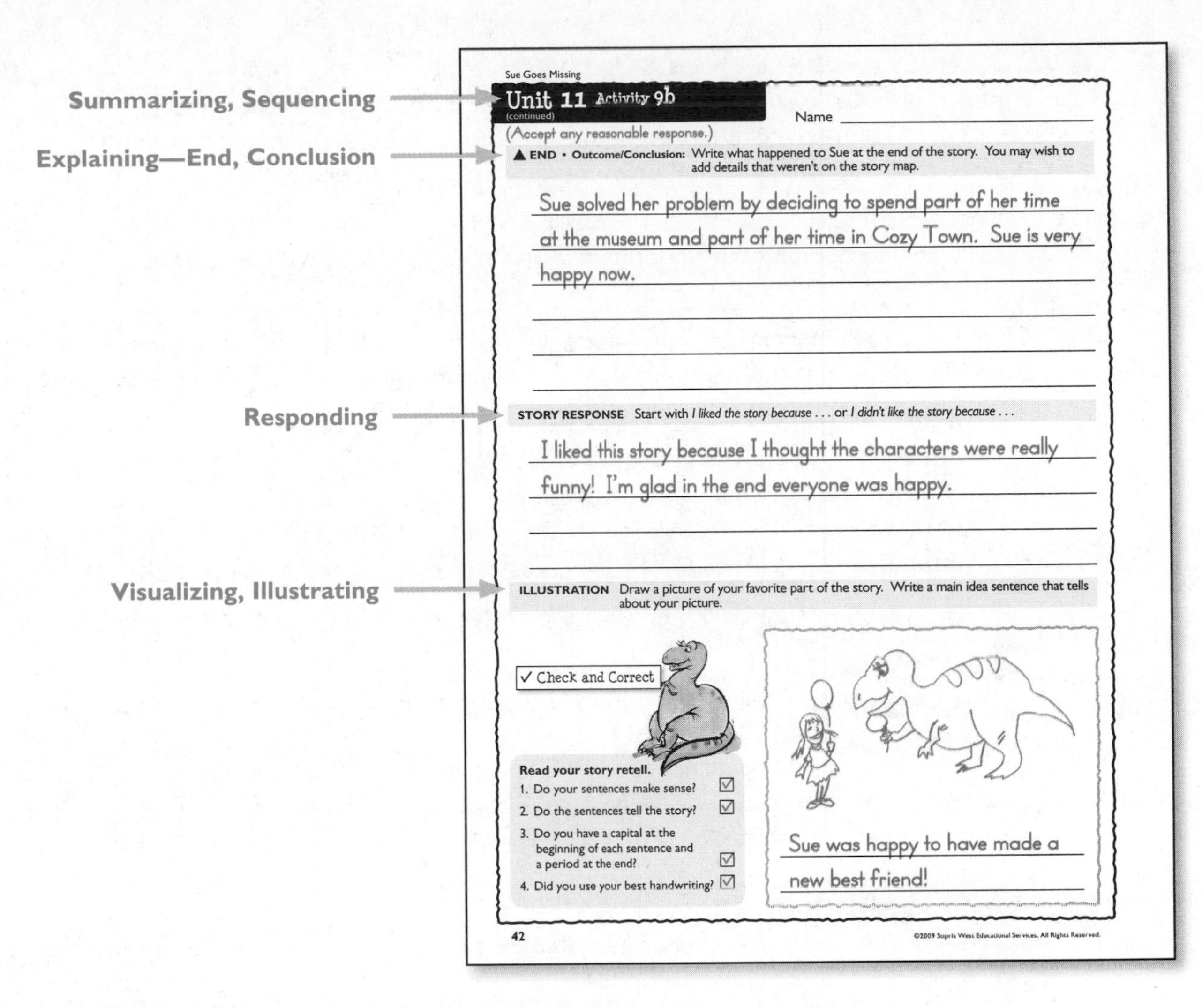

Written Retell: Paragraph Writing—Basic Instructions *(continued)*

- Guide students as they construct an ending paragraph based on information in the story map.
- Have students write a complete sentence explaining why they liked or did not like the story.
- Have students check and correct their work, then visualize and illustrate their favorite part of the story.

❶ SOUND REVIEW

Have students read the sounds and key word phrases in each row. Work for accuracy, then fluency.

❷ ACCURACY AND FLUENCY BUILDING

- For each task, have students say any underlined part, then read the word.
- Set a pace. Then have students read the whole words in each task and column.
- Provide repeated practice, building accuracy first, then fluency.

D1. Word Endings

Have students read the underlined word, then the word with an ending.

E1. Tricky Words

- For each Tricky Word, have students use the sounds and word parts they know to silently sound out the word. Use the word in a sentence to help with pronunciation.

field The middle school team was practicing on the high school football . . . *field.*
done He was glad when he had finished his homework and was finally . . . *done.*
though It won't snow today. It may rain . . . *though.*
woman's The hat belonged to the woman. It was the . . . *woman's* . . . hat.
museum Jackson liked looking at the paintings in the art . . . *museum.*

- Have students go back and read the whole words in the column.

E2. Story Words

For each word, tell students the underlined sound and have them read the word. Use the word in a sentence, as needed.

August In some places, the hottest month of the summer is . . . *August.*
giant In *Jack and the Beanstalk,* Jack stole magic items from the . . . *giant.*
enormous Another word for really, really big is . . . *enormous.*

❸ MULTISYLLABIC WORDS

For each word, have students read the syllables, then the whole word. Use the word in a sentence, as appropriate.

complete All the pieces were in the puzzle. It was . . . *complete.*
expedition The explorers went to the North Pole on an . . . *expedition.*
located The missing ring was found. It was . . . *located.*
skeleton There are lots of bones in the human . . . *skeleton.*
whether He didn't know if he would go. He didn't know . . . *whether* . . . he would go.
realized He suddenly knew the answer. He just . . . *realized* . . . it.

❹ WORDS IN CONTEXT

Tell students to use the sounds and word parts they know to silently sound out the word. Then have students read the sentence. Assist, as needed.

❺ MORPHOGRAPHS AND AFFIXES

- Have students read the underlined part, then the word.
- Repeat practice with whole words, mixing group and individual turns. Build accuracy, then fluency.

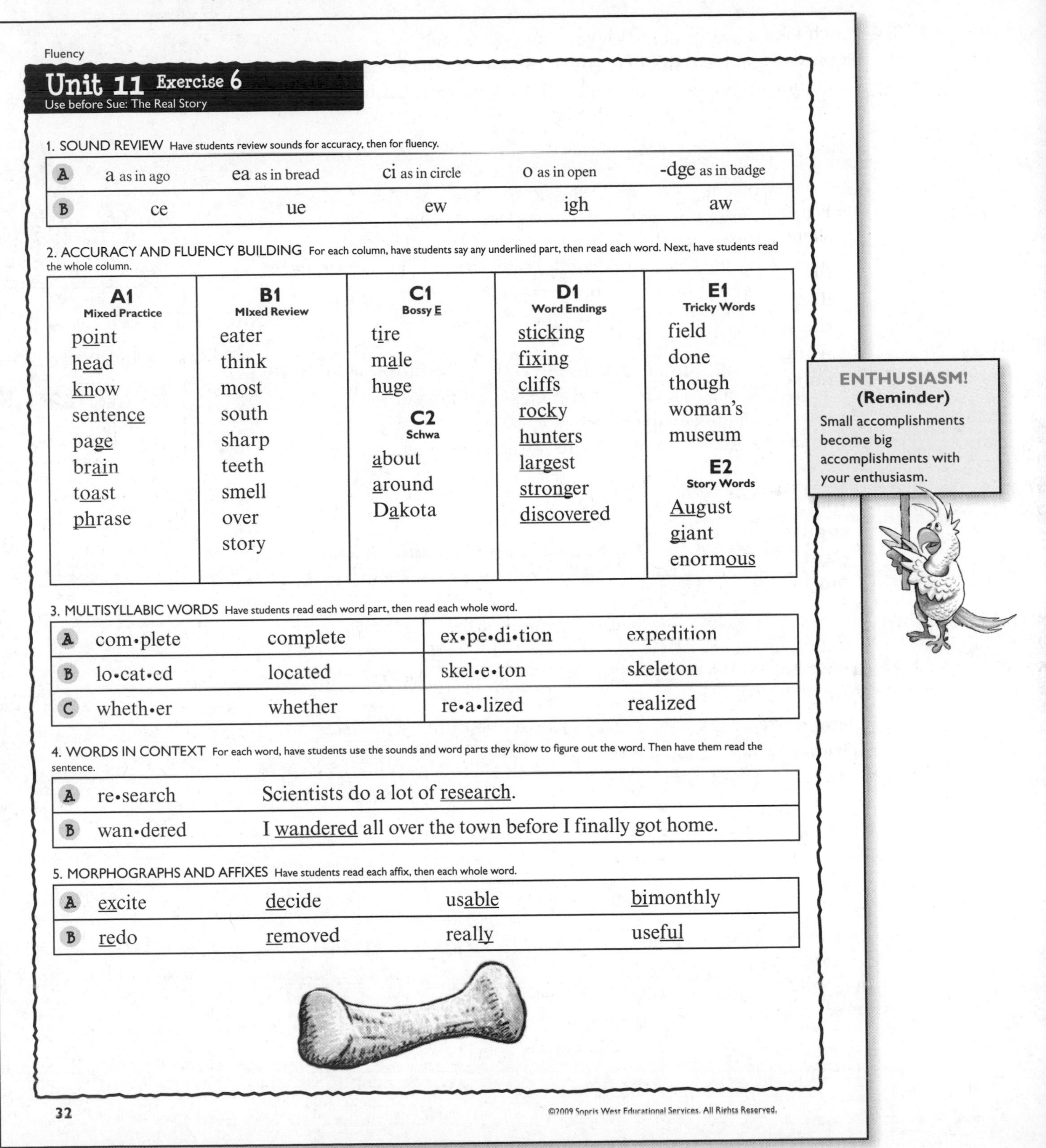

Fluency

Unit 11 Exercise 6
Use before Sue: The Real Story

1. SOUND REVIEW Have students review sounds for accuracy, then for fluency.

A	a as in ago	ea as in bread	ci as in circle	o as in open	-dge as in badge
B	ce	ue	ew	igh	aw

2. ACCURACY AND FLUENCY BUILDING For each column, have students say any underlined part, then read each word. Next, have students read the whole column.

A1 Mixed Practice	B1 Mixed Review	C1 Bossy E	D1 Word Endings	E1 Tricky Words
point	eater	tire	sticking	field
head	think	male	fixing	done
know	most	huge	cliffs	though
sentence	south	**C2 Schwa**	rocky	woman's
page	sharp	about	hunters	museum
brain	teeth	around	largest	**E2 Story Words**
toast	smell	Dakota	stronger	August
phrase	over		discovered	giant
	story			enormous

3. MULTISYLLABIC WORDS Have students read each word part, then read each whole word.

A	com•plete	complete	ex•pe•di•tion	expedition
B	lo•cat•ed	located	skel•e•ton	skeleton
C	wheth•er	whether	re•a•lized	realized

4. WORDS IN CONTEXT For each word, have students use the sounds and word parts they know to figure out the word. Then have them read the sentence.

A	re•search	Scientists do a lot of research.
B	wan•dered	I wandered all over the town before I finally got home.

5. MORPHOGRAPHS AND AFFIXES Have students read each affix, then each whole word.

A	excite	decide	usable	bimonthly
B	redo	removed	really	useful

32

©2009 Sopris West Educational Services. All Rights Reserved.

ENTHUSIASM! (Reminder)

Small accomplishments become big accomplishments with your enthusiasm.

FLUENCY PASSAGE INSTRUCTIONS

This Story Reading targets fluency as the primary goal of instruction and practice. Students do Repeated Readings of this short passage to improve accuracy, expression, and rate.

PROCEDURES

1. Warm-Up: Partner Reading or Whisper Reading

Before beginning group Story Reading, have students finger track and partner or whisper read the selection.

2. First Reading

- Ask questions as indicated by the gray text.
- Mix group and individual turns, independent of your voice. Have students work toward a group accuracy goal of 0–3 errors. Quietly keep track of errors made by all students in the group.
- After reading the story, practice any difficult words. Reread the story if students have not reached the accuracy goal.

PARTNER READING— CHECKOUT OPPORTUNITY

While students are doing Partner Reading, listen to individuals read the passage. Work on accuracy and fluency, as needed.

3. Second Reading, Short Passage Practice: Developing Prosody

- Demonstrate reading the first paragraph with expression and fluency. Have students finger track as you read.
- Have students choral read the first paragraph. Encourage reading with expression and fluency.
- Repeat with second paragraph.

4. Third Reading, Group Timed Readings: Repeated Reading

- Encourage each child to work for a personal best. Have students whisper read for a one-minute Timed Reading. Tell students to go back to the top of the page and keep reading until the minute is up.
- Have students put their finger on the last word they read and count the number of words read correctly in one minute.
- Have students do a second Timed Reading of the same page.
- Have students try to beat their last score.
- Celebrate improvements.

5. Written Assessment (Comprehension and Skill)

Tell students they will do a Written Assessment after they read "Sue: The Real Story." (For teacher directions, see pages 87 and 88.)

6. Homework 6: Repeated Reading

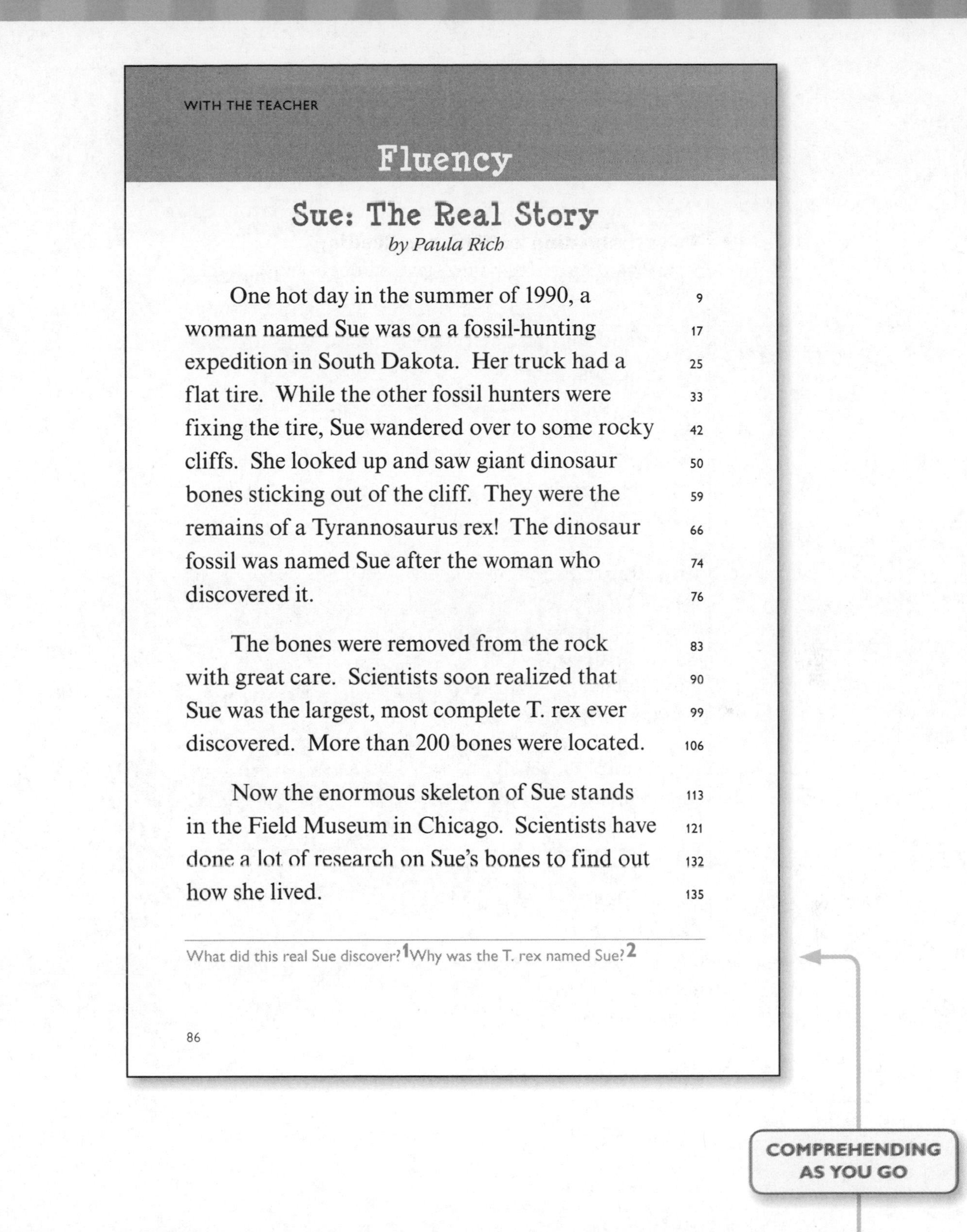

WITH THE TEACHER

Fluency

Sue: The Real Story

by Paula Rich

One hot day in the summer of 1990, a 9
woman named Sue was on a fossil-hunting 17
expedition in South Dakota. Her truck had a 25
flat tire. While the other fossil hunters were 33
fixing the tire, Sue wandered over to some rocky 42
cliffs. She looked up and saw giant dinosaur 50
bones sticking out of the cliff. They were the 59
remains of a Tyrannosaurus rex! The dinosaur 66
fossil was named Sue after the woman who 74
discovered it. 76

The bones were removed from the rock 83
with great care. Scientists soon realized that 90
Sue was the largest, most complete T. rex ever 99
discovered. More than 200 bones were located. 106

Now the enormous skeleton of Sue stands 113
in the Field Museum in Chicago. Scientists have 121
done a lot of research on Sue's bones to find out 132
how she lived. 135

What did this real Sue discover?[1] Why was the T. rex named Sue?[2]

86

COMPREHENDING AS YOU GO

❶ **Remember:** Identifying—What; Using Vocabulary—fossil (Sue discovered the bones of a T. rex. Sue found a fossil.)

❷ **Understand:** Explaining (Sue discovered the fossil, so they named it after her.)

Scientists have learned that the part of Sue's brain used for smell was huge, so we know that the sense of smell was probably very important to a T. rex. Sue's teeth were very large, strong, and sharp, so scientists think Sue was probably a meat eater. 8 18 26 36 44 47

One thing we can't tell from the fossil is whether Sue was male or female. Even though Sue now has a woman's name, we don't know if she really was a she! 56 64 74 79

What did the scientists learn from the bones?[1]

COMPREHENDING AS YOU GO

❶ **Understand:** Summarizing (The part of the dinosaur's brain used for smell was huge. Its teeth were large, strong, and sharp. The T. rex was probably a meat eater.)

WRITTEN ASSESSMENT

COMPREHENSION PROCESSES

Remember, Understand, Apply

WRITING TRAITS

Word Choice
Conventions—Complete Sentence, Capital, Period
Presentation

Test Taking

Identifying—Main Character, Narrator
Sentence Completion

Using Vocabulary—frantic

Identifying—Problem

Identifying—Action

Inferring

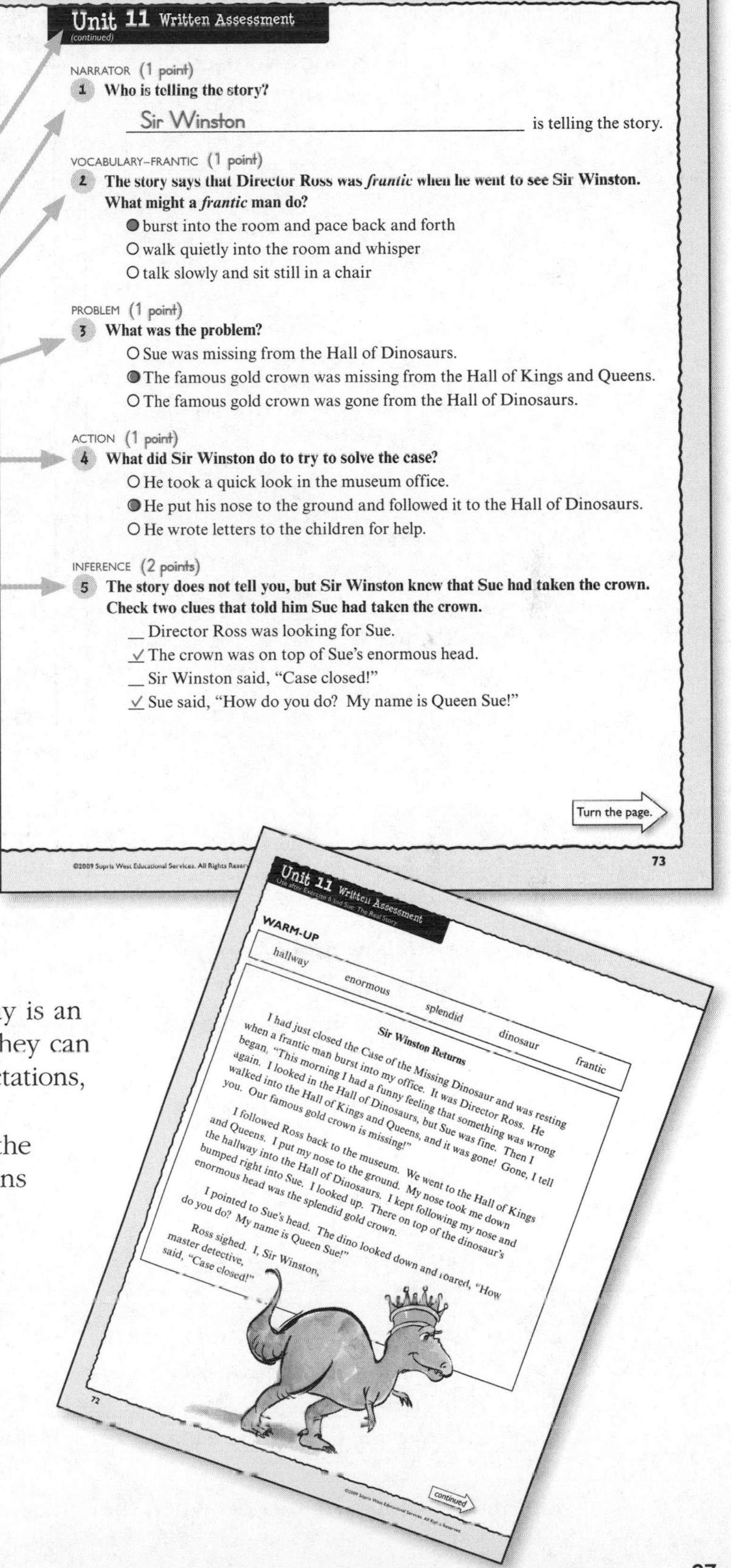

Unit 11 Written Assessment (continued)

NARRATOR (1 point)

1 Who is telling the story?

Sir Winston is telling the story.

VOCABULARY–FRANTIC (1 point)

2 The story says that Director Ross was *frantic* when he went to see Sir Winston. What might a *frantic* man do?

- ● burst into the room and pace back and forth
- O walk quietly into the room and whisper
- O talk slowly and sit still in a chair

PROBLEM (1 point)

3 What was the problem?

- O Sue was missing from the Hall of Dinosaurs.
- ● The famous gold crown was missing from the Hall of Kings and Queens.
- O The famous gold crown was gone from the Hall of Dinosaurs.

ACTION (1 point)

4 What did Sir Winston do to try to solve the case?

- O He took a quick look in the museum office.
- ● He put his nose to the ground and followed it to the Hall of Dinosaurs.
- O He wrote letters to the children for help.

INFERENCE (2 points)

5 The story does not tell you, but Sir Winston knew that Sue had taken the crown. Check two clues that told him Sue had taken the crown.

- __ Director Ross was looking for Sue.
- ✓ The crown was on top of Sue's enormous head.
- __ Sir Winston said, "Case closed!"
- ✓ Sue said, "How do you do? My name is Queen Sue!"

Turn the page.

73

Unit 11 Written Assessment
Use after Exercise 6 and Sue: The Real Story

WARM-UP

hallway enormous splendid dinosaur frantic

Sir Winston Returns

I had just closed the Case of the Missing Dinosaur and was resting when a frantic man burst into my office. It was Director Ross. He began, "This morning I had a funny feeling that something was wrong again. I looked in the Hall of Dinosaurs, but Sue was fine. Then I walked into the Hall of Kings and Queens, and it was gone! Gone, I tell you. Our famous gold crown is missing!"

I followed Ross back to the museum. We went to the Hall of Kings and Queens. I put my nose to the ground. My nose took me down the hallway into the Hall of Dinosaurs. I kept following my nose and bumped right into Sue. I looked up. There on top of the dinosaur's enormous head was the splendid gold crown.

I pointed to Sue's head. The dino looked down and roared, "How do you do? My name is Queen Sue!"

Ross sighed. I, Sir Winston, master detective, said, "Case closed!"

72

continued

PROCEDURES

Do not demonstrate or guide practice.

Written Assessment—Introductory Instructions

1. Introduce the Written Assessment.
   - Remind students that their work today is an opportunity for them to show what they can do independently. Clarify your expectations, as needed.
   - Tell students they will whisper read the passage and then answer the questions without help.

WRITTEN ASSESSMENT (*continued*)

Describing—Character Traits (Characterization); Sentence Writing

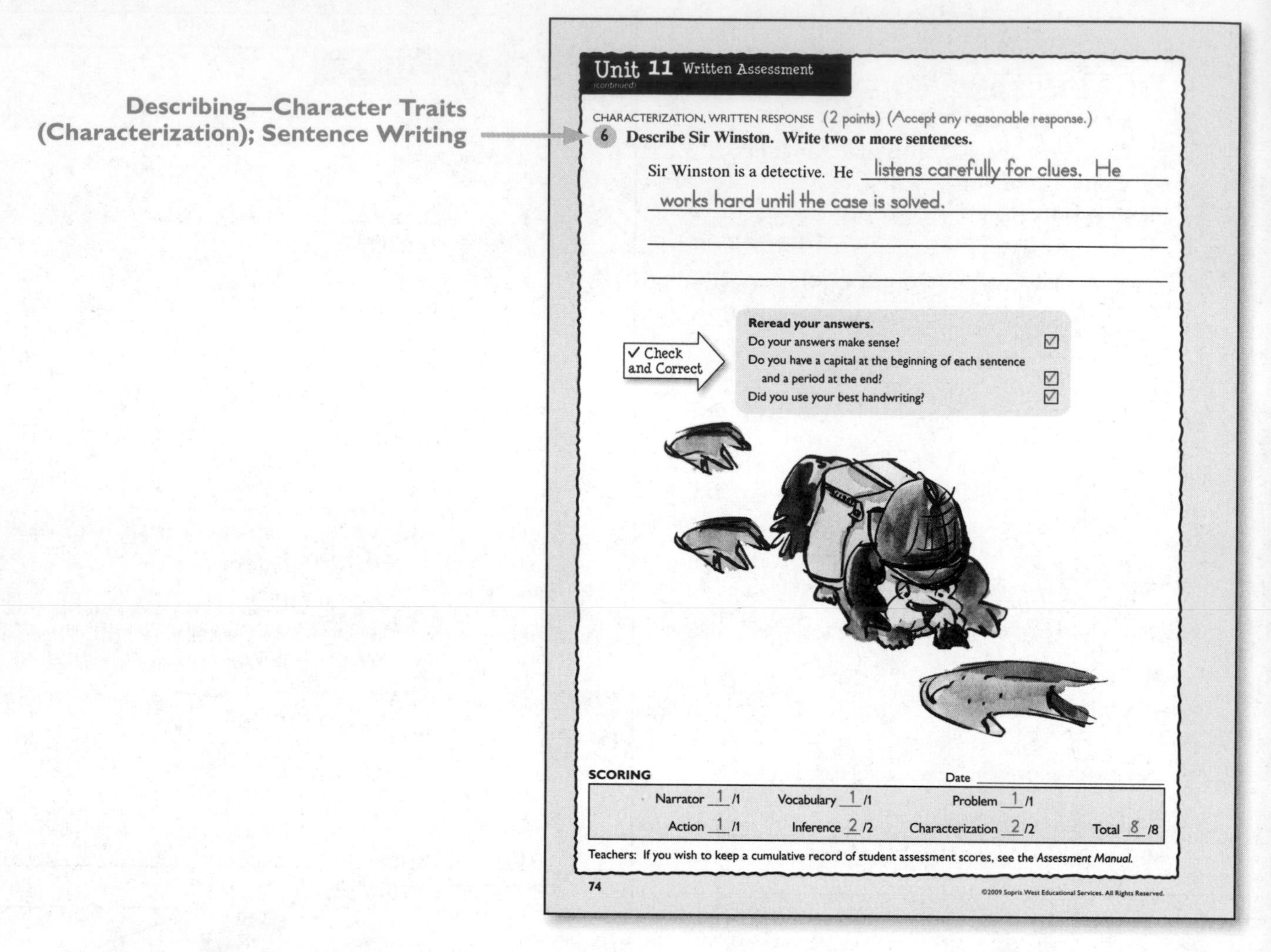

Unit 11 Written Assessment (continued)

CHARACTERIZATION, WRITTEN RESPONSE (2 points) (Accept any reasonable response.)

6 Describe Sir Winston. Write two or more sentences.

Sir Winston is a detective. He listens carefully for clues. He works hard until the case is solved.

✓ Check and Correct

Reread your answers.

- Do your answers make sense? ☑
- Do you have a capital at the beginning of each sentence and a period at the end? ☑
- Did you use your best handwriting? ☑

SCORING Date ____

Narrator 1 /1	Vocabulary 1 /1	Problem 1 /1	
Action 1 /1	Inference 2 /2	Characterization 2 /2	Total 8 /8

Teachers: If you wish to keep a cumulative record of student assessment scores, see the *Assessment Manual.*

74 ©2009 Sopris West Educational Services. All Rights Reserved.

2. Check for student understanding.
   Say something like:
   Look at your assessment. What are you going to do first? (write my name)

   What are going to do next? (whisper read the passage)
   What will you do after you read the passage? (answer the questions)

   That's great. Now what will you do if you get to a hard question?
   (reread the question and try again)
   That's right. What should you do if it's still hard? (reread the passage and try again)
   Very good. And if you still aren't sure, what will you do? (do my best and keep going)

3. Remind students to check and correct.
   When you finish your assessment, what should you do? (check and correct)
   That's right. Go to the top of the page. Reread the questions and make sure your answers make sense. Fix anything that doesn't sound right. Make sure you have an answer for every question.

4. Remind students what to do when they finish their work.

End of the Unit

In this section, you will find:

Making Decisions

As you near the end of the unit, plan to give the Written Assessment and the Oral Reading Fluency Assessment to each child in your group. Use this section as a general guide for making instructional decisions and doing diagnostic planning.

Written Assessment

The Unit 11 Written Assessment is located on page 71 of *Activity Book 2* and on the CD.

Oral Reading Fluency Assessment

The Unit 11 Oral Reading Fluency Assessment is located on page 93 of this teacher's guide and in the *Assessment Manual.*

Certificate of Achievement

Celebrate your children's accomplishments. When your students master the unit skills, send home the Certificate of Achievement.

Extra Practice Lessons

Use the Extra Practice lessons for students who need additional decoding and fluency work. Student materials can be copied from the Extra Practice blackline masters.

Making Decisions

GENERAL ASSESSMENT GUIDELINES

1. After students read Story Reading 6, "Sue: The Real Story," give the group the Unit 11 Written Assessment in place of Comprehension and Skill Work. Follow the instructions on pages 87 and 88 of this guide.

2. While the group is completing the Written Assessment or any time during the day, administer the Oral Reading Fluency Assessment. Assess each student individually.

   Optional: Graph the results of the assessment. (See Unit 7 Teacher's Guide, pages 92 and 95.)
   - If the student's words correct per minute go up, congratulate the student.
   - If the student's words correct per minute go down, discuss the student's overall improvement and help him or her identify ways to improve for the next assessment.

3. Score oral fluency responses on the Student Assessment Record. Adhere to the scoring criteria in the *Assessment Manual.* Use a stopwatch to time how long it takes each student to read the Oral Reading Fluency Passage, and record errors.

USING THE WRITTEN ASSESSMENT RESULTS

Results of the Written Assessment *should not* be used to determine whether a student or group of students continues forward in the program. As long as students pass the Oral Reading Fluency Assessment, they should continue forward with the next unit.

The Written Assessment should be used to informally monitor how well students read independently and answer questions in writing. If any student has difficulty with the Written Assessment, re-administer the assessment orally.

If the student has difficulty answering the questions orally:
- Record the types of errors (e.g., main idea, sequencing, open-ended response).
- Provide explicit instruction for these types of questions during reading group, before independent work, and in tutorials, as needed.
  1. Demonstrate (or model) appropriate responses, guide practice, and provide opportunities for independent practice.
  2. For inferential questions, think aloud with students—explain how you arrive at an answer.
  3. For literal questions, teach students to reread a passage, locate information, reread the question, and respond.

At this level, if the student is able to answer the questions orally but not on paper, it may not be due to comprehension problems. The student's difficulties may be related to a lack of motivation, an inability to work independently, or a struggle with handwriting, spelling, language, or vocabulary.

USING THE ORAL READING FLUENCY RESULTS

At the end of each unit, you will need to make decisions regarding student progress. Should students go forward in the program? Does the group need Extra Practice before proceeding?

Do individuals require more assistance and practice to continue working in their group? These decisions all require use of the oral reading fluency data and professional judgment. As you analyze assessment results, watch for trends and anomalies.

See the *Assessment Manual* for detailed information and instructional recommendations. General guidelines and recommendations follow:

Strong Pass ≥ 111 WCPM 0–2 errors	• Continue with the current pace of instruction. • Have students set goals. (Until students are reading approximately 180 words correct per minute, oral reading fluency continues to be an instructional goal.)
Pass 89–110 WCPM 0–2 errors	• Continue with the current pace of instruction. Consider increasing fluency practice.
No Pass ≤ 88 WCPM **RED FLAG** A No Pass is a red flag. A mild early intervention can prevent an intense and time-consuming intervention in the future.	• If a child scores a No Pass but has previously passed all assessments, you may wish to advance the student to the next unit, then carefully monitor the student. • If a child scores a No Pass but has previously passed all assessments, you may wish to advance the student to the next unit and also provide additional practice opportunities. (See below.) • If a child scores two consecutive No Passes or periodic No Passes, additional practice must be provided. (See below.) • If a child scores three consecutive No Passes, the student should be placed in a lower-performing group.

Added Practice Options for Groups

Warm-Ups:

- Begin each lesson with Partner Reading of the previous day's homework.
- Begin each day with Partner Reading of a Word Fluency from Extra Practice.
- Begin each lesson with a five-minute Fluency Booster. Place copies of the Unit 5–10 *Read Well* Homework in three-ring notebooks. Each day, have students begin Finger Tracking and Whisper Reading at Unit 5, Homework 1. At the end of five minutes, have students mark where they are in their notebooks. The next day, the goal is to read farther.
- Begin each Story Reading with a review of the previous day's story.
- After reading the story, include Short Passage Practice on a daily basis.

Extended Units: If several children begin to score No Passes or barely pass, extend the unit by adding Extra Practices 1, 2, and/or 3. Extra Practice lessons include Decoding Practice, Fluency Passage, Word Fluency, and a Comprehension and Skill Activity. (See pages 95–100 in this guide.)

Jell-Well Reviews: A Jell-Well Review is the *Read Well* term for a review of earlier units. A Jell-Well Review is a period of time taken to celebrate what children have learned and an opportunity to firm up their foundation of learning. To complete a Jell-Well Review, take the group back to the last unit for which all students scored Strong Passes. Then quickly cycle back up. See the *Assessment Manual* for how to build a Jell-Well Review.

Added Practice Options for Individual Students

Tutorials: Set up five-minute tutorials on a daily basis with an assistant, trained volunteer, or cross-age tutor. Have the tutor provide Short Passage Practice and Timed Readings or Extra Practice lessons.

Double Dose: Find ways to provide a double dose of *Read Well* instruction.

- Have the student work in his or her group *and* a lower-performing group.
- Have an instructional assistant, older student, or parent volunteer preview or review lessons.
- Have an instructional assistant provide instruction with Extra Practice lessons.
- Preview new lessons or review previous lessons.

END-OF-THE-UNIT CELEBRATION

When students pass the Oral Reading Fluency Assessment, celebrate with the Certificate of Achievement on page 94.

Note: Using the Flesch-Kincaid Grade Level readability formula, the Unit 11 Assessment has a 2.5 readability level. Readability formulas provide only a rough estimate of difficulty. Just adding one or two multisyllabic words to the passage can increase the readability by one or two months.

TRICKY WORD and FOCUS SKILL WARM-UP

point	breakfast	Howie	believe	climb	entrance

ORAL READING FLUENCY PASSAGE

The Amazing Dinosaur

★My brother Howie and I were excited. Mom was taking 10
us to the big museum to see the dinosaur fossils. First, she made 23
us eat breakfast. Then we put on our coats and walked to the 36
train station. We all climbed on the train for the long trip into the 50
city. 51

Finally, Mom said, "We're here!" We jumped off the 60
train. Mom knew the way to the museum. When we saw the 72
museum, Howie and I could hardly believe our eyes. It was 83
huge! 84

We hopped up the steps and walked through the front 94
doors. Howie gave me a nudge and pointed. "Look, Sue's over 105
there!" An enormous skeleton of an extinct T. rex stood near the 117
entrance. Howie and I ran over to look at it. We felt as small as 132
ants next to Sue. It was really amazing! 140

ORAL READING FLUENCY Start timing at the ★. Mark errors. Make a single slash in the text (/) at 60 seconds. Have the student complete the passage. If the student completes the passage in less than 60 seconds, have the student go back to the ★ and continue reading. Make a double slash (//) in the text at 60 seconds.

WCPM Determine words correct per minute by subtracting errors from words read in 60 seconds.

STRONG PASS The student scores no more than 2 errors on the first pass through the passage and reads 111 or more words correct per minute. Proceed to Unit 12.

PASS The student scores no more than 2 errors on the first pass through the passage and reads 89 to 110 words correct per minute. Proceed to Unit 12.

NO PASS The student scores 3 or more errors on the first pass through the passage and/or reads 88 or fewer words correct per minute. Provide added fluency practice with *RW2* Unit 11 Extra Practice. (Lessons follow the certificate at the end of the teacher's guide.) After completing the Extra Practice, retest the student.

You Did It!

____

has successfully completed

Read Well* 2 Unit 11 • *Dog Detective

with ______ words correct per minute.

Teacher Signature ______________________

Date ______________________

You Did It!

____

has successfully completed

Read Well* 2 Unit 11 • *Dog Detective

with ______ words correct per minute.

Teacher Signature ______________________

Date ______________________

PROCEDURES

CAUTION

Your children may not need Extra Practice. Use assessment results to determine if Extra Practice is needed.

1. Sound Review

Use selected Sound Cards from Units 1–11.

2. Sounding Out Smoothly

- For each word, have students say the underlined part, sound out the word smoothly, then read the whole word. Use the words in sentences, as needed.
- Repeat practice. Mix group and individual turns, independent of your voice.

3. Accuracy and Fluency Building

- For each task, have students say any underlined part, then read each word.
- Set a pace. Then have students read the whole words in each task and column.
- Repeat practice, building accuracy first, then fluency.

4. Tricky Words

Have students read each row for accuracy, then for fluency.

5. Multisyllabic Words

For each word, have students read each syllable out loud, finger count the syllables, then tell how many syllables are in the word. If needed, use the word in a sentence. Have students read the whole word.

EXTRA PRACTICE 1

Unit 11 Decoding Practice

Name ____________________

1. SOUND REVIEW Use selected Sound Cards from Units 1–11.

2. SOUNDING OUT SMOOTHLY Have students say the underlined part, sound out and read each word, then read the row.

seems	while	short	long

3. ACCURACY/FLUENCY BUILDING Have students say any underlined part, then read each word. Next, have students read the column.

A1 Sound Practice	B1 Word Endings	C1 Bossy E	D1 Tricky Word Buildups
voice soil join head read across about find kind	dig digging large largest point pointy asked hardly	take taking amaze amazing ate fascinate fascinating excited decided describe	cover covered uncovered **D2** Mixed Practice remains Henry Winston fossil creature

4. TRICKY WORDS Have students read each row for accuracy, then fluency.

A	brother	eye	through	front	weigh	5
B	question	aha	very	what	figure	10

5. MULTISYLLABIC WORDS Have students read the word by parts, tell how many syllables are in the word, then read the whole word.

A	ques•tion	question	de•tec•tive	detective
B	car•ni•vore	carnivore	skel•e•ton	skeleton
C	def•i•nite•ly	definitely	Brach•i•o•saur•us	Brachiosaurus

6. DICTATION Say the word. Have students say the word, then finger count and say the sounds. Have students say each sound as they touch or write it.

A1 Shifty Words	B1 Rhyming Words
b a r k s h ar k sh ar p	j u m p b u m p l u m p

73

6. Dictation

bark, shark, sharp, jump, bump, lump

- Say "bark." Have students say the word. Guide students as they finger count and say the sounds. Have students touch or write the sounds, then read the word. Say something like:

  The first word is ***bark.*** Say the word. (bark) Say and count the sounds in ***bark*** with me. **Hold up one finger for each sound.** /b/•/ar/•/k/ How many sounds? (three)

  What's the first sound? (/b/) Touch under /b/.
  What's the next sound? (/ar/) Write /ar/.
  What's the last sound? (/k/) Touch under /k/.
  Read the word. (bark)

- Repeat with "shark" and "sharp."
- Continue with the rhyming words: jump, bump, lump.

PROCEDURES

1. **First Reading**

   Have students work toward an accuracy goal of 0–2 errors and practice any difficult words.

2. **Second Reading, Short Passage Practice: Developing Prosody**
   - Demonstrate how to read a line or two.
   - Guide practice with your voice.
   - Provide individual turns while others track with their fingers and whisper read.

3. **Partner Reading: Repeated Reading (Checkout Opportunity)**

   While students do Partner Reading, listen to individuals read the passage. Work on accuracy and fluency, as needed.

4. **Homework: Repeated Reading**

PROCEDURES • ACTIVITY, WORD FLUENCY A

Demonstrate and guide practice, as needed.

1. **Activity**

   Passage Comprehension
   - Have students read each sentence or question, then fill in and/or check the blank with the correct answer.
   - Think aloud with students and discuss the multiple-choice options, as needed.

   Paragraph Comprehension
   - Have students read the paragraph.
   - Have students read each numbered sentence, fill in the bubble and/or blank, then read the completed sentences.

2. **Word Fluency (BLMs are located on the CD.)**
   - To build fluency, have students read each section three times in a row.
   - To build accuracy, have students read all sets with partners.

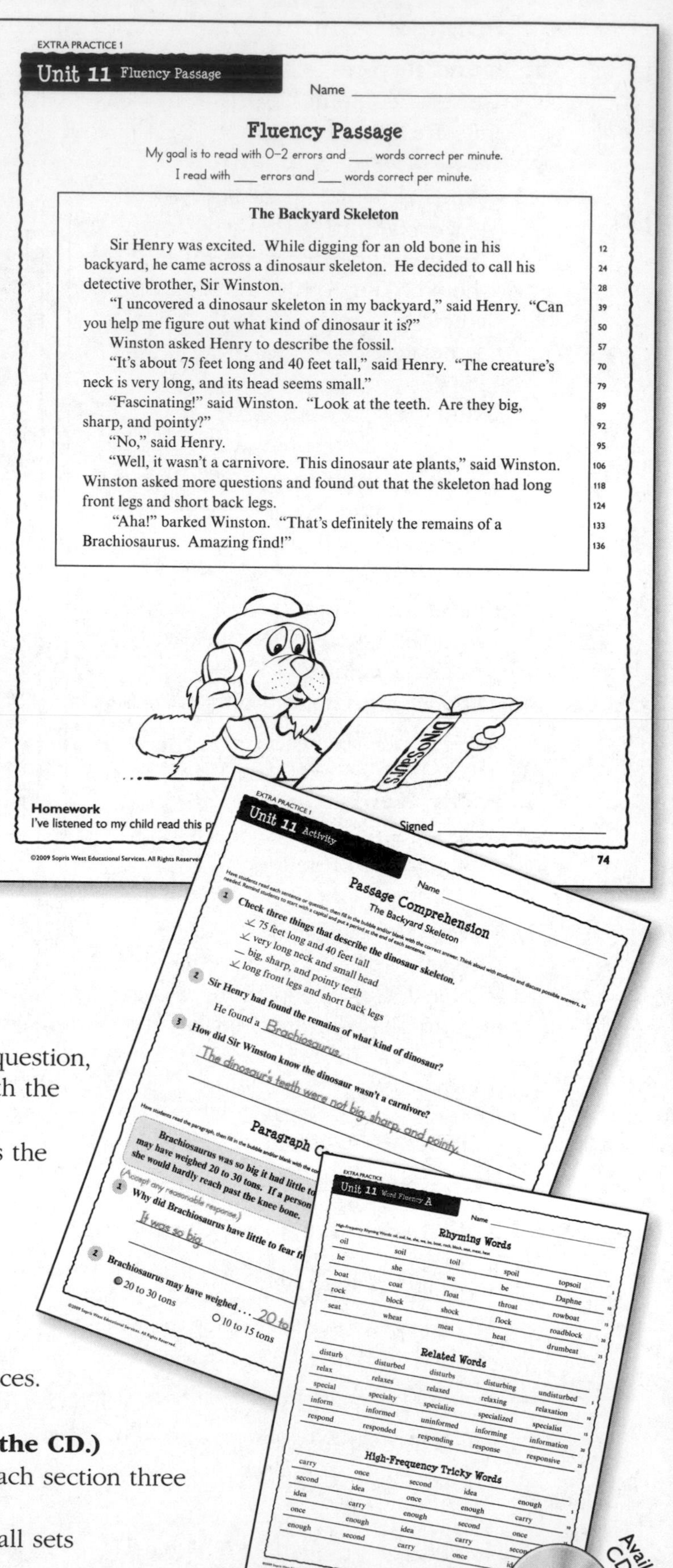

EXTRA PRACTICE 1

Unit 11 Fluency Passage

Name ____________________

Fluency Passage

My goal is to read with 0–2 errors and ___ words correct per minute.

I read with ___ errors and ___ words correct per minute.

The Backyard Skeleton

Sir Henry was excited. While digging for an old bone in his	12
backyard, he came across a dinosaur skeleton. He decided to call his	24
detective brother, Sir Winston.	28
"I uncovered a dinosaur skeleton in my backyard," said Henry. "Can	39
you help me figure out what kind of dinosaur it is?"	50
Winston asked Henry to describe the fossil.	57
"It's about 75 feet long and 40 feet tall," said Henry. "The creature's	70
neck is very long, and its head seems small."	79
"Fascinating!" said Winston. "Look at the teeth. Are they big,	89
sharp, and pointy?"	92
"No," said Henry.	95
"Well, it wasn't a carnivore. This dinosaur ate plants," said Winston.	106
Winston asked more questions and found out that the skeleton had long	118
front legs and short back legs.	124
"Aha!" barked Winston. "That's definitely the remains of a	133
Brachiosaurus. Amazing find!"	136

Homework

I've listened to my child read this p... Signed ____________

74

EXTRA PRACTICE 1

Unit 11 Activity

Name ____________

Passage Comprehension

The Backyard Skeleton

1. Check three things that describe the dinosaur skeleton.
   - ✓ 75 feet long and 40 feet tall
   - ✓ very long neck and small head
   - ___ big, sharp, and pointy teeth
   - ✓ long front legs and short back legs
2. Sir Henry had found the remains of what kind of dinosaur?

   He found a Brachiosaurus.
3. How did Sir Winston know the dinosaur wasn't a carnivore?

   The dinosaur's teeth were not big, sharp, and pointy.

Paragraph C...

Brachiosaurus was so big it had little t... may have weighed 20 to 30 tons. If a person... she would hardly reach past the knee bone.

1. Why did Brachiosaurus have little to fear f...

   (Accept any reasonable response.) It was so big.
2. Brachiosaurus may have weighed . . . 20 to...
   - ● 20 to 30 tons
   - ○ 10 to 15 tons

EXTRA PRACTICE

Unit 11 Word Fluency A

Name ____________

Rhyming Words

oil	soil	toil	spoil	topsoil
he	she	we	be	Daphne
boat	coat	float	throat	rowboat
rock	block	shock	flock	roadblock
seat	wheat	meat	heat	drumbeat

Related Words

disturb	disturbed	disturbs	disturbing	undisturbed
relax	relaxes	relaxed	relaxing	relaxation
special	specialty	specialize	specialized	specialist
inform	informed	uninformed	informing	information
respond	responded	responding	response	responsive

High-Frequency Tricky Words

carry	once	second	idea	enough
second	idea	once	enough	carry
idea	carry	enough	second	once
once	enough	idea	carry	secon...
enough	second	carry	once	id...

PROCEDURES

1. Sound Review

Use selected Sound Cards from Units 1–11.

2. Sounding Out Smoothly

- For each word, have students say the underlined part, sound out the word smoothly, then read the whole word. Use the words in sentences, as needed.
- Repeat practice. Mix group and individual turns.

3. Accuracy and Fluency Building

- For each task, have students say any underlined part, then read each word.
- Set a pace. Then have students read the whole words in each task and column.
- Provide repeated practice, building accuracy first, then fluency.

4. Tricky Words

Have students read each row for accuracy, then fluency.

EXTRA PRACTICE 2

Unit 11 Decoding Practice

Name ____________________

1. SOUND REVIEW Use selected Sound Cards from Units 1–11.

2. SOUNDING OUT SMOOTHLY Have students say the underlined part, sound out and read each word, then read the row.

coat	laid	know	kept

3. ACCURACY/FLUENCY BUILDING Have students say any underlined part, then read each word. Next, have students read the column.

A1 Sound Practice	B1 Word Endings	C1 Rhyming Words	D1 Related Words
dead read spread point oil voice	baby babies colony colonies sitting hopped hatched looked	thought bought brought	cover covering discover
A2 Compound Words		**C2** Bossy E	**D2** Sound Review
into basketball		bones alone close size here	after over ever together

4. TRICKY WORDS Have students read each row for accuracy, then fluency.

A	area	warm	young	often	you	5
B	mother	climbed	they	could	learn	10

5. MULTISYLLABIC WORDS Have students read the word by parts, tell how many syllables are in the word, then read the whole word.

A	sci•en•tists	scientists	e•nor•mous	enormous
B	mu•se•um	museum	fi•nal•ly	finally
C	sev•er•al	several	prob•a•bly	probably

6. DICTATION Say the word. Have students say the word, then finger count and say the sounds. Have students say each sound as they touch or write it.

A1 Shifty Words	B1 Rhyming Words
e gg e gg s l e g s	n e s t b e s t r e s t

 76

5. Multisyllabic Words

For each word, have students read each syllable out loud, finger count the syllables, then tell how many syllables are in the word. If needed, use the word in a sentence. Have students read the whole word.

> **CAUTION**
> Your children may not need Extra Practice. Use assessment results to determine if Extra Practice is needed.

6. Dictation

egg, eggs, legs, nest, best, rest

- Say "eggs." Have students say the word. Guide students as they finger count and say the sounds. Have students touch or write the sounds, then read the word.

The first word is **egg.** Say the word. (egg) Say and count the sounds in **egg** with me.

Hold up one finger for each sound. /ĕĕĕ/•/ggg/ How many sounds? (two)

What's the first sound? (/ĕĕĕ/) Write /ĕĕĕ/.
What's the next sound? (/ggg/) Touch under /ggg/.
Read the word. (egg)

- Repeat with "eggs" and "legs."
- Continue with the rhyming words: nest, best, rest.

PROCEDURES

1. **First Reading**
   Have students work toward an accuracy goal of 0–2 errors and practice any difficult words.

2. **Second Reading, Timed Reading: Repeated Reading**

   - Time individual students for 30 or 60 seconds while the other children track with their fingers and whisper read.
   - Determine words correct per minute. Record student scores.

3. **Partner Reading: Repeated Reading (Checkout Opportunity)**

   While students do Partner Reading, listen to individuals read the passage. Work on accuracy and fluency, as needed.

4. **Homework: Repeated Reading**

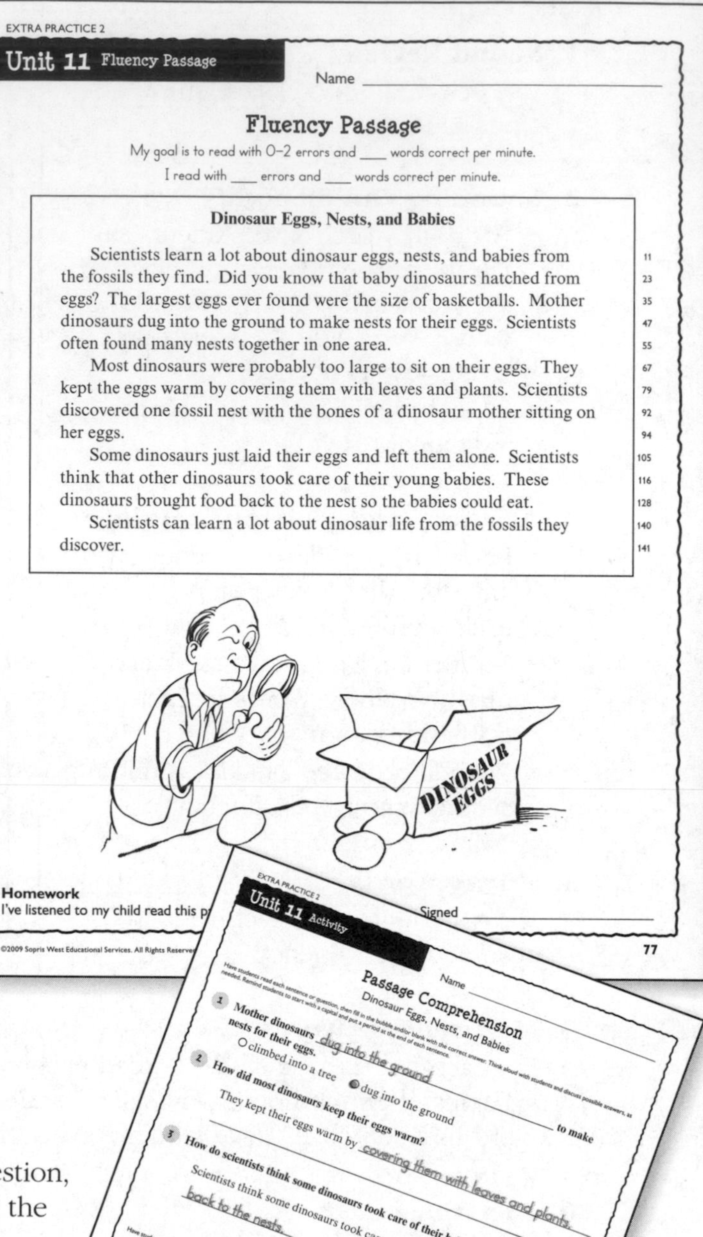

EXTRA PRACTICE 2

Unit 11 Fluency Passage

Name ____________

Fluency Passage

My goal is to read with 0–2 errors and ___ words correct per minute.

I read with ___ errors and ___ words correct per minute.

Dinosaur Eggs, Nests, and Babies

Scientists learn a lot about dinosaur eggs, nests, and babies from the fossils they find. Did you know that baby dinosaurs hatched from eggs? The largest eggs ever found were the size of basketballs. Mother dinosaurs dug into the ground to make nests for their eggs. Scientists often found many nests together in one area. 11 23 35 47 55

Most dinosaurs were probably too large to sit on their eggs. They kept the eggs warm by covering them with leaves and plants. Scientists discovered one fossil nest with the bones of a dinosaur mother sitting on her eggs. 67 79 92 94

Some dinosaurs just laid their eggs and left them alone. Scientists think that other dinosaurs took care of their young babies. These dinosaurs brought food back to the nest so the babies could eat. 105 116 128

Scientists can learn a lot about dinosaur life from the fossils they discover. 140 141

Homework
I've listened to my child read this p... Signed ____________

 77

PROCEDURES • ACTIVITY, WORD FLUENCY B

Demonstrate and guide practice, as needed.

1. **Activity**
   Passage Comprehension
   - Have students read each sentence or question, then fill in the bubble and/or blank with the correct answer.
   - Think aloud with students and discuss the multiple-choice options, as needed.

   Paragraph Comprehension
   - Have students read the paragraph.
   - Have students read each numbered sentence, fill in the bubble and/or blank, then read the completed sentences.

2. **Word Fluency (BLMs are located on the CD.)**
   - To build fluency, have students read each section three times in a row.
   - To build accuracy, have students read all sets with partners.

Available on CD-ROM

PROCEDURES

1. **Sound Review**
   Use selected Sound Cards from Units 1–11.

2. **Sounding Out Smoothly**
   - For each word, have students say the underlined part, sound out the word smoothly, then read the whole word. Use the words in sentences, as needed.
   - Have students read all the words in the row, building accuracy first, then fluency.
   - Repeat practice. Mix group and individual turns.

3. **Accuracy and Fluency Building**
   - For each task, have students say any underlined part, then read each word.
   - Set a pace. Then have students read the whole words in each task and column.
   - Repeat practice, building accuracy first, then fluency.

EXTRA PRACTICE 3

Unit 11 Decoding Practice

Name ______________________

1. SOUND REVIEW Use selected Sound Cards from Units 1–11.

2. SOUNDING OUT SMOOTHLY Have students say the underlined part, sound out and read each word, then read the row.

nudge	throw	knew	saw

3. ACCURACY/FLUENCY BUILDING Have students say any underlined part, then read each word. Next, have students read the column.

A1 Sound Practice	B1 Word Endings	C1 Rhyming Words	D1 Tricky Words
point soil	reply replied	train explain remain	anything something everything nothing
excite city	finding	**C2** Bossy E	
little chuckle	cleaned turned solved puzzled	made make huge here	Howie neighbor believe specialty
around away	dashed jumped	retrace	breakfast

4. TRICKY WORDS Have students read each row for accuracy, then fluency.

A	we're	put	pulled	living	gone	5
B	brother	your	where	walked	key	10

5. MULTISYLLABIC WORDS Have students read the word by parts, tell how many syllables are in the word, then read the whole word.

A	real•ly	really	ex•tinct	extinct
B	fran•tic	frantic	skel•e•ton	skeleton
C	en•trance	entrance	sta•tion	station

6. DICTATION Say the word. Have students say the word, then finger count and say the sounds. Have students say each sound as they touch or write it.

A1 Shifty Words	B1 Rhyming Words
c a s e	i n s i d e
c a v e	o u t s i d e
g a v e	d e c i d e

79

4. **Tricky Words**
   Have students read each row for accuracy, then fluency.

5. **Multisyllabic Words**
   For each word, have students read each syllable out loud, finger count the syllables, then tell how many syllables are in the word. If needed, use the word in a sentence. Have students read the whole word.

CAUTION

Your children may not need Extra Practice. Use assessment results to determine if Extra Practice is needed.

6. **Dictation**

   case, cave, gave, inside, outside, decide
   - Say "case." Have students say the word. Guide students as they finger count and say the sounds. Have students touch or write the sounds, then read the word.

   The first word is ***case.*** Say the word. (case) Say and count the sounds in ***case*** with me.
   Hold up one finger for each sound. /k/•/āāā/•/sss/ How many sounds? (three)
   What's the first sound? (/k/) Touch under /k/.
   What's the next sound? (/aaa/) Write /āāā/.
   What's the next sound? (/sss/) Touch under /sss/.
   Read the word. (case) Yes, the Bossy E at the end makes letter a say its name.

   - Repeat with "cave" and "gave."
   - Continue with the rhyming words: inside, outside, decide.

PROCEDURES

1. First Reading

Have students work toward an accuracy goal of 0–2 errors and practice any difficult words.

2. Second Reading, Short Passage Practice: Developing Prosody

- Demonstrate how to read a line or two.
- Guide practice with your voice.
- Provide individual turns while others track with their fingers and whisper read. Provide descriptive and positive feedback.

3. Partner Reading: Repeated Reading (Checkout Opportunity)

While students do Partner Reading, listen to individuals read the passage. Work on accuracy and fluency, as needed.

4. Homework: Repeated Reading

EXTRA PRACTICE 3

Unit 11 Fluency Passage

Name ________________

Fluency Passage

My goal is to read with 0–2 errors and ___ words correct per minute.

I read with ___ errors and ___ words correct per minute.

The Case of the Missing Keys

Detective Winston had a new case to solve. His neighbor Rex had	12
lost his keys and was frantic to find them. Finding things was Winston's	25
specialty.	26
"Where did you see them last?" asked Winston.	34
"I was in the living room. The keys were in my hand. Then they	48
were gone," said Rex.	52
"Let's retrace your steps," said Winston. "What did you do in the	64
living room?"	66
"I turned on the TV," said Rex. So Winston looked around the TV.	79
Nothing there.	81
"Then what did you do?" asked Winston.	88
"I cleaned up a little," Rex replied.	95
"Did you throw anything away?"	100
"Maybe," Rex said, looking a little puzzled. Winston dashed over	110
to the small trash can by the desk. He looked inside and pulled out	124
Rex's keys.	126
"I think you did throw something away," Sir Winston said with a	138
chuckle. Case solved!	141

Homework

I've listened to my child read this p... Signed ________________

80

PROCEDURES • ACTIVITY, WORD FLUENCY A OR B

For each step, demonstrate and guide practice, as needed. Then have students complete the page independently.

1. Activity

Passage Comprehension

- Have students read each sentence or question, then fill in the bubble and/or blank with the correct answer.
- Think aloud with students and discuss the multiple-choice options, as needed.

Paragraph Comprehension

- Have students read the paragraph.
- Have students read each numbered sentence, then fill in the bubble and/or blank.
- Have students read the completed sentences.

EXTRA PRACTICE 3

Unit 11 Activity

Name ________________

Passage Comprehension

The Case of the Missing Keys

1. Winston was very good at finding things. What's another way to say that?
   - ● Winston's specialty was finding things.
   - ○ Winston was frantic at finding things.
   - ○ Winston was puzzled at finding things.
2. Detective Winston asked Rex to *retrace his steps* to find his keys.
   - ○ turn on the TV ● retrace his steps ○ clean up a little
3. Where were the keys found?
   The keys were found in the trash can.

Paragraph Comprehension

Rex went to the museum with his friend Ann. At the end of the day, Ann was missing. Rex wanted to be a detective just like Winston. He retraced his steps back through the museum and found Ann with the dinosaurs!

(Accept any reasonable response.)

1. Why did Rex retrace his steps back through the museum?
   He retraced his steps to *be a detective like Sir Winston.*
2. Do you think Rex is as good a detective as Winston? Why or why not?
   Yes. Rex is a good detective. He found Ann.

✓ Check and Correct

81

2. Word Fluency (BLMs are located on the CD.)

You may wish to have students repeat practice with Extra Practice Word Fluency A or B.